Aether

The
Transcript

This work is the transcript of an original audio recording
produced by M I Finesilver and published
simultaneously by Pathway (Initiatives) Ltd.

Acknowledgements
and Thanks

Thanks again to all the main contributors/speakers on the recording, in particular Nick Thomas.

To Valery Rees, thanks for help and contribution regarding Marsilio Ficino.

Thanks to Richard Adams, for permission to reproduce the passage from *The Iron Wolf* (1980).

To Thames and Hudson Ltd, for permission to reproduce the passage from Tao, The Chinese Philosophy of Time and Change by Philip Rawson and Laszlo Legeza, 1973.

To Marilyn Finlay, special thanks for being both very professional and very obliging regarding all the recording sessions. Thanks to Chris Robins, Brieve Lyon and Joe Peter for assistance with recording.

Thanks for your much valued input, Nelson Willby, Paul Carline, Malin Starrett, Julie Carter.

Thanks also to: Carla Finesilver (flute), Jon Ramster, David Dansky, Judith Gregory, Hugh Hoffman, Justin Underhill (Premen), Joseph Finlay, Belinda Henson, Martin Wacey, Roy Wilkinson and Tony Hannaford.

And a very special thanks to Jacqueline for the additional writing and all the invaluable editing, general help and encouragement throughout.

Contributors

N C (Nick) Thomas, independent scientist, mathematician, 17 years an RAF electrical engineering officer, authority on aetheric technology

Dr Edi Bilimoria, consultant engineer for the Channel Tunnel, London Underground and other major projects

Dr Margaret Colquhoun, biologist/ecologist, Executive Director of *The Life Science Trust* UK

Patrick Dixon, actor, esotericist, speaker

Dr Geoffrey Douch, GP, homeopath, anthroposophical doctor

Professor Brian Goodwin, biologist, Open University, University of Sussex, Schumacher College UK

David Lorimer, teacher and Programme Director of *The Scientific and Medical Network*

Laurence Newey, esotericist

Yiannis Pittis, healer, clairvoyant, Director of the *Philalethia College of Healing*

Professor Ian J Thompson, Physics, at the University of Surrey UK

Michael Watson, independent scientist, electrical engineer and avionics engineer in the design of the Concorde aircraft, authority on aetheric technology

John Wilkes, sculptor, inventor of *Flowforms*, Director of the *Virbela Research Institute*

Professor Arthur Zajonc, Physics, at Amherst College USA

The contributors were recorded between 2004 and 2006 with the exception of two earlier recordings, one of Nick Thomas and one of Arthur Zajonc.

CONTENTS

What is this Aether?

NT: I think one has to become involved.

I don't think that's an issue now, for me. It was at one time.

For years I didn't become involved, because I was concerned about possible misuse. But then life brought it towards me from different directions and I had to. And I recognise that.

And so I think now that it's not a question of whether you become involved – I think you have to – if you're in my line of business, that is.

'Out of the Aether!'

'*The idea just came to me out of the Aether*', it's often said.

Or we speak of information and messages travelling '*through the Aether*', and of things unaccountably vanishing '*into the Aether*'.

What is this Aether? And where exactly are all these ideas and messages floating and flying about?

It seems that the Aether would have to be everywhere. So does it actually exist? Or is it merely a figure of speech?

NT: There are certain things in this world that really need to be known about more widely – if we want to understand it and our place in it better.

Our education institutions, our scientific institutions, our religious institutions – none of these really teach this vital thing: the nature and significance of the Aether.

The Aether is not a familiar or obvious subject to approach at first. The whole project could be seen as an exercise in following up various clues... leading to the rediscovery of some powerful, well concealed knowledge – knowledge that affects all areas of our lives.

Why a secret?

And, inevitably, a further question arises:

How come the Aether has been so effectively excluded from our mainstream culture for so long, despite an Internet search in 2006 finding several million very diverse references to it? (That is, including the two alternative spellings.)

This question will become a significant part of our enquiry as the bigger picture emerges.

The Internet itself can be seen as an outer, materialized symbol of the inner developments that are taking place in human consciousness. The essence of the Internet is its *non-locality* and *continuous connectedness*, both of which are characteristics of the Aether and ideas at the heart of Quantum physics.

The global brand name *Ethernet* – for a system which connects up networks of computers – illustrates this point. Then there's *Cyberspace*, a very real, yet intangible and infinite, realm of ideas and information, accessible through the hard-wired hardware and the ever-evolving software of the Internet. And like the Aether, it's available to all who have the know-how and the means to access it.

A common question

A common question arising in this work has been:

Since you can't see, hear, touch, taste or smell it, what difference would a clearer awareness of the Aether make to my life?

One brief answer goes like this:

Imagine that you've been taught and you believe that the Earth is not spherical but flat – with all the implications that would follow from this denial. You could still get by on a day to day level, but your whole outlook would be severely limited and distorted.

Powerful new knowledge can sometimes seem threatening but we have to be prepared always to question the status quo, since this whole cosmos is perpetually in a state of change.

Independent

This project is a completely independent venture, owing no allegiance to any organization. It has been produced on a very low budget and without any fancy visuals, dramatic effects or even a fictionalised plotline. It's simply offered as the combined thoughts of a few straight talking people who know that it's the attitude, the motives and assumptions behind the questions we ask, that determine the kind of answers we get. And they do ask some pertinent questions for our time, regardless of how these may be responded to, officially or unofficially.

The contributors

You'll hear from a number of people, all well qualified in their own areas of work or study, who each have something significant to say regarding our opening questions about the Aether. As individuals, they may not completely agree with all the other views expressed, but they do share a strong common purpose.

Their differences enrich the project – in the way that *bio-diversity* makes for a healthy ecosystem. And when the essentials of each are pinpointed and the dots joined up, as it were, then a clear picture emerges.

And here, by way of introduction, are the voices of the main contributors to this project:

N C (Nick) Thomas independent scientist, mathematician, an electrical engineering officer in the RAF for 17 years, an authority on aetheric technology:

> **'It's the Aether that gives us life. It's the Aether that gives us vitality. It's the Aether that makes us healthy or ill. Or at least it**

has a huge role to play in all of that. And if we have no idea what the Aether is then obviously we're going to judge these things in a false way.'

Professor Arthur Zajonc, Physics, at Amherst College, USA:

'We stand in an open field, we look out into the blue of the sky and we ask the question which every child asks: Why is the sky blue?'

Professor Ian J Thompson, Physics, at the University of Surrey, UK:

'There's another kind of process in physics which has often also been identified with Aether, and this is the idea of 'zero point motion' – the fact that in a vacuum there are many things which appear to be happening, or potentially happening, but not actually happening. And this has often been thought of as the Aether. Because it's what's in the world when there are no material objects.'

Dr Margaret Colquhoun, biologist/ecologist, executive director of *The Life Science Trust*, UK :

'One thing that's very interesting is that I've met quite a few people who, when they start doing this kind of training on the development of their relationship or use of Aethers within themselves, they grow. And that's a very extraordinary phenomenon, as a middle-aged adult, to find that your hand size, your head size, your feet size...is all getting bigger.'

Professor Brian Goodwin, Biology, at the Open University, University of Sussex, and now at Schumacher College:

'We've strutted around in our culture as controllers and dominators of the Earth. And the result is, the earth is going through a pretty drastic transition that's going to challenge our culture very deeply.'

Michael Watson, Independent scientist, electrical engineer and avionics engineer in the design of the Concorde aircraft:

> 'The Aether is not just an abstract force like electricity is. It's got this mobility inside it which electricity doesn't have.'

Dr Edi Bilimoria, consultant engineer for the Channel Tunnel, London Underground and other major projects:

> 'You can have something that's very precise that's totally fallacious. You can have the graph to twenty-one decimal points. You can build an Eiffel Tower of logic on very shaky sands. And the logic and the superstructure can be impregnable but it'll topple over if your fundamental assumptions are shaky.'

David Lorimer, teacher, writer and programme director of *The Scientific and Medical Network:*

> 'Scientists act as philosophers. They say philosophical things. And you cannot divorce science from its metaphysical context Because if you don't make your philosophy explicit then it's going to remain implicit. Because you cannot exist without having a set of assumptions which you operate from.'

Patrick Dixon, actor, esotericist, speaker:

> 'A knowledge of the aetheric in the arts will open up vistas both of the universe in a completely new way, but also give the individual localised personality a tremendously great context out of which they move and develop.'

Laurence Newey, esotericist:

> 'We can expand our idea of the Aether by also considering it in terms of fire. And we find the idea of 'celestial fire' in the ancient Greek concept of aither, the fifth element.'

Yiannis Pittis, healer, clairvoyant, teacher:

> 'Aetheric vision - anybody really can begin to trigger it. It's not so difficult. Everyone, when we do some lectures on healing or aura and so on, I give a simple practice, and then we have pretty much a ninety-nine per cent success of everybody being able to see the 'aetheric body' - that glow that is around the physical form.'

John Wilkes, sculptor, inventor, research scientist in water enhancement:

> 'Real investigation of real things started in the realm of modern art. That's not abstract at all!'

Dr Geoffrey Douch, GP, homeopath, anthroposophical doctor:

> 'In a way, it's only the effects of the aetheric forces that you can study.'

What connects the contributors is a compelling awareness that **something vital is missing** from our present Western culture, and therefore from our lives in the Western and westernized world. Whether qualified in the sciences, the arts, teaching or in medical and healing work, each of the contributors has courageously followed his or her intuitive knowing.

The contributors are referred to as courageous because it does require considerable inner strength and integrity to refuse to unquestioningly comply with the requirements of the status quo and instead, seriously question it.

Similarly, it takes courage to try and counter what's being programmed into young minds in the name of mass education - which includes, of course, teacher training.

They've made it a priority, some even their life's quest, to recover the missing knowledge, the key to the lost meaning of our lives - that intermediate level between the earthly and the cosmic, between the material and the spiritual.

It's as though certain vital pages of the manual have somehow gone missing.

And the vital missing factor, we suggest, is **awareness of the Aether.**

In other words

In our language, various terms have been substituted for the missing Aether. For example, we speak of an 'air of celebration', a 'highly charged atmosphere', someone having an 'air of grace' about them, or a radio station being 'on air'. We speak of the 'chemistry' between people which is really the alchemy of qualities, which is itself actually about aethereal processes.

Then there's the 'thrill' of anticipation or excitement as we await the indefinable, magical 'X factor' in a performance. All these physical-material terms are used poetically to describe our experiencing of the aethereal realm.

Meanwhile, there are any number of industries and professions providing an endless supply of substitutes – for the insatiable demand, the worldwide addictive hunger for that missing fulfilment, meaning and magic.

The search for the 'missing something' has been given form in stories of quests – some portrayed in highly popularized epic movies and novels. These have dealt, for example, with superhuman forces and powers, the blurring of the boundaries between real and imaginary worlds, ideological conflicts, and love lost and found. The stories of Western medicine and science – from alchemy to our present dilemmas - can similarly be seen as *quests*... as will become apparent in this project.

Another familiar aethereal phenomenon is what's known as the *ethos* of any organisation – be it a family, a gang or some other set up. Briefly, it's the unspoken set of assumptions, rules and conventions which govern what is and what is not acceptable behaviour within it.

There are certain basic principles governing the functioning of the cosmos. And achieving harmony with these is what some have called the *science of being* and the *art of living*.

In a culture of death

We talk about life and living as if we know what we mean. But the fierce conflict between Church and medical science about the beginning and end of individual lives reminds us how little we really know. We can see in our materialistic Western world what amounts to a *denial of life*, such that we've ended up with a *culture of death*.

We seem caught in its grip – as exemplified in the fascination with murder mysteries, medical dramas and war stories.

This is a consequence of lost Aether awareness.

In the continuous recycling of living Nature, *physical death* can be understood as a process of progressive *releasing* or *shedding*. Our individual aetheric body is absorbed back into the greater ocean of the Aether. And what was the living physical body is left as inanimate, disintegrating matter to be reunited with the Earth.

The process then continues with our more subtle levels of being.

Aliveness

According to both the ancient and our modern wholistic understanding, the primary quality of the Aether is that of *aliveness, livingness, vitality* – the difference between you and a corpse. Life itself.

And what characterizes all living forms is that:

(1) they are *conscious* and act with purpose, beyond seeking mere physical survival or storing and applying information, and

(2) they *pulsate*: they rhythmically *expand* and *contract*, *breathe in* and *breathe out*, *grow* and *shrink*. And it's this interplay between *polar* opposites, within any system, that demonstrates the universal principle of *polarity* – something we find throughout all Nature and the cosmos.

also known as

Awareness of the *Aether* under different names, and ideas about it, go back into the farthest reaches of human history. *Aether* comes from an ancient Greek word, and one of its many meanings is: 'the substance that permeates the cosmos from which the stars and planets were made'. It also signifies *a blazing, the heavens, shining light* and *the upper atmosphere*.

Sambhoga-kaya, an ancient Tibetan term, refers to the intermediate stage in the emerging of the cosmos. From the nothingness or unity state emanated radiant light, which then evolved into this physical universe. Indian and Chinese culture have various names for different aspects of the Aether. In the Hebrew Old Testament it's referred to as the 'cosmic waters'.

Plato and Aristotle spoke of the non-material Aether, as did Sir Isaac Newton, Albert Einstein and even Max Planck, the founder of Quantum Physics.

It's also alluded to in hymns which speak of inspirational light, fire and radiance... and in the literary works of Milton, Keats, Wordsworth and Shelley.

The influential Renaissance philosopher Marsilio Ficino wrote, "....*the force of the World-soul is spread....through all things through the quintessence, which is active everywhere, as the spirit inside the World's Body....*"

Quintessence, which literally means the *fifth essence* or element, is another ancient term which has recently been re-introduced into modern physics. It refers to the subtle, indefinable, universal something that pervades the whole cosmos.

One eminent physicist, David Bohm, seemed very close to the idea of the Aether when he proposed a non-physical realm of potential manifestation. This he called the *implicate order*, which exists as the middle level of a three-level system. And another well known contemporary scientist and writer, Paul Davies, has suggested the concept of a *quantum ether*.

So despite various authoritative dismissals – including articles in the *Encyclopaedia Britannica* – the true Aether never really did go away.

Here's **Nick Thomas** talking about the most recent falling from favour of the Aether... and its inevitable re-emergence.

NT: In the 19th century people thought that light had to have something to travel through, just as sound travels through air. It was thought that you can't have light just travelling; light must travel through something. And so they invented the Aether as a sort of perfect medium, and then ran into problems, because the various experiments that I spoke about earlier, of light having a constant apparent velocity, don't work very well with that world outlook. And by the time the 19th century physicists had finished with it, the Aether was an impossibly perfect substance that couldn't exist really.

And so there was a huge sigh of relief when Einstein managed to come up with an alternative explanation that didn't need this 'luminiferous ether', as they called it. And so they were delighted to push it to one side. Einstein himself never actually did, as far as I am aware. He simply accounted for phenomena in his way.

So, having got rid of it, the last thing they wanted was another one. So when science had shaken off the shackles of the 'ether' at the beginning of the 20th century, they didn't want another one pushed on them straight away! And so somehow one had to go through eighty, ninety years of freedom from the ether, you see.

But now we've got new younger generations, we've got new experimental results, and they're all pointing to something which cannot be accounted for without it.

Four Aethers in one

Within the one Aether, four distinguishable levels have been identified.

The primary level, known as the *Warmth Aether*, is all about the power of fire and heat to transform substance into different states.

The next level, moving inwards from periphery towards centre, is the *Light Aether*. This is concerned with the division into polarities, such as the opposing qualities of dark and light, density and rarity.

The third level inwards is variously known as the *Tone, Number, Chemical, Sound* or *Colour Aether*. And it's the key to appreciating the deeper significance of the gradations and patterns that constitute music, mathematics, chemistry, alchemy and much more.

The fourth level is known as the *Life Aether*, and it's about the meaning of the countless, separate, physical-material forms of our world in all its diversity.

One example of *aethereal* quality is the *ambience* or atmosphere that can be created through the magical power of music and colour.

Individually, each living being has a subtle *aetheric body* which permeates and animates the physical form.

17

So the Aether is not sterile chemistry or physics. Nor is it just an old idea loaded with religious overtones. It's very much a reality that people felt they knew in a very immediate way, before this present era of our highly developed, analytical, quantifying, precise, machine mentality.

Aether is one of those big, inclusive words, like *world, ocean* and *mind.*

Esoteric and Occult

Being non-material and, therefore, not accessible to our physical senses, the Aether is what's known as *esoteric.* It could also be called *occult* – which means hidden. This level of thinking is more about intuitive sensing and inferring than about intellectual reasoning and hard evidence.

Here are a few *esoteric* and *occult* angles on the Aether.

First you'll hear **Patrick Dixon** who was responding to questions, and then excerpts from **Laurence Newey** who was delivering a scripted talk.

Esoteric Aspects of the Aether
Patrick Dixon and Laurence Newey

PD: The Aetheric, really, is a dimension of reality, the Aetheric, which is not acknowledged by modern science. This Aetheric refers to what the ancient Indian cultures, the Yogic, Chinese, call *prana* or *chi*, which is the energy body, which permeates the physical body and distinguishes the living, for instance the plant or the animal, from the mineral, which is dead, to all intents and purposes.

One could say that the Aetheric body manifests itself through the movements, the hidden movements within living beings that distinguish them from dead ones – for instance circulation of the blood, the movement of sap within trees – not visible from the outside but essential for the maintainance of the life form.

LN: The Aether is the one universal lying behind all manifestation.

Aether is a universal matrix from which spring many active currents, given various titles descriptive of various qualities and functions. And in turn these active currents are the cause of the elements of Air, Fire, Water and Earth and the labyrinth of created forms.

Down the ages, different philosophies have given Aether a multitude of names to differentiate its many aspects.

PD: The Aetheric world is also subdivided into four principles, you could say four levels, four manifestations of activity.

Of course, they are not completely separate. They are like colours in the spectrum. They blend into each other and work across each other. And they work also at different times of the day more strongly on the Earth. And at different seasons of the year different Aethers will be working more predominantly.

LN: We can expand our idea of the Aether by also considering it in terms of fire. And we find the idea of 'celestial fire' in the Ancient Greek concept of *aither*, the fifth element.

Like that of the sun, the radiative heat of *aither* was thought to be the pure essence where the Gods lived and which they breathed. The word derives from *aith*, meaning 'fire' or 'burn' and, sounding similar to the word aether, we have the combination of fire and vital energy which gives us a good description of the nature of Aether.

To get a more esoteric understanding, we could first imagine a vast 'sea of fire' as the subtlest form of universal substance. To further develop this image, let us picture the active heat moving in the sea of fire and causing areas of accumulation and consequent precipitation. Beneath the 'sea of fire' this creates a plane of manifestation known as the *akasha*. This plane has come into being through the accretion of fire into masses of burning light. And indeed, it can be thought of as 'the plane of the flaming suns.' As active heat causes the *akasha* to spiral on downwards, the planes below take form, on which human and super-human evolution occurs.

PD: On a very very high level, if you work on yourself, then you no longer have a personal Aetheric body. You have a universal Aetheric body. So therefore, when you die you don't have to lose it. Your individuality becomes part of the universal planetary Akashic chronicle – on a higher level.

LN: The idea of the Aether is scattered throughout sacred Hindu scriptures such as the Upanishads, the Puranas and the Vedas; and in Mahayana Buddhism we have the concept of 'generative emptiness', the void known as *S'unyata*. But many Westerners will be familiar with the notion of Aether through popular Chinese and Indian disciplines such as Tai Chi, Feng Shui, acupuncture and Yoga. The Chinese disciplines have their roots in Taoist philosophy and its teaching about the universal life force, *chi*. And while they may address widely different areas, they all work by harmonising the flow of *chi* in the body and the surrounding environment. The Hindu equivalent of this chi would be *prana*, that part of the Aether actively circulating throughout manifestation.

Whereas science tells us that all is energy and that energy and matter are interchangeable, ancient philosophies tell us that the 'divine breath' is all. Spirit and matter being modifications of this 'divine breath in motion' are therefore, in essence, one and the same thing: matter is spirit in its densest expression, and spirit is matter in its most rarefied state.

For ease of understanding then, we can regard spirit as a sublime form of energy, and in turn, what is generally termed the aether can be described as a sublime form of matter – the true substance that lies behind matter as science understands it, that interpenetrates and actuates all forms.

PD: Most people use the words soul, spirit, but don't know exactly what they mean. There's no defined understanding of it. There is a very strong connection between what we call the soul and the Aetheric body in a way, because the soul is connected also with memory.

If you can imagine all the experiences of the human being, both in and out of the body, through many incarnations, creates this kind of resonant space which is called 'the soul,' *becomes* the soul. And it is a huge mine, a treasure house, a reservoir of experiences which eventually will be taken up on another level. And that's the experience you get through memory. Memory always activates the soul. Recollection is about 'loading the Ark up' to take the memories, the experiences, into the future.

And the reason why this is connected with the Aetheric body is, the Aetheric body has two essential functions. One is to maintain the life processes of the body – that is to say, the circulation of forces throughout the body, maintain the connection between the different poles and organs of the body. And the other function of the Aetheric body is to take perceptions down and, you could say, download them into deep memory. This is really the nourishment which actually feeds, you could say, the 'living museum of the soul.' So the Aetheric body is actually the Ark which takes in perceptions and personalises them and eventually eternalises them.

That's one of the reasons why we grow old – because the 'loading up of the ship' causes a kind of... it's like a tape being overloaded with perceptions, pictures, which then slows down the cosmic pictures that drive the life processes within the human body. So the experiences you have on the Earth then displace the pictorial plan of movement that the cosmos puts into us, in our Aetheric body when we are born.

That's why, if you do the *Rückschau*, you actually clear the tapes to a certain extent so that you free up the Aetheric body again, which can then rejuvenate the life processes. (*Rückschau* is the meditation at the end of the day when you go backwards through the day to the beginning. You can do it at any time of the day but essentially its a recollection.) That's an anticipation of the *kamaloka* experience when, after death, you go backwards through your life. So if you do the *Rückschau* a lot, you're already in that experience so you shorten that experience. The interesting thing is the connection between the soul, the memory and the Aetheric body.

LN: 'In the Beginning was the Word', and this brings to our attention the role of sound in the creation of the manifest universe. Sound is the dominant creative aspect associated with pure *akasha*. The 'Word of God' is emitted from and through *akasha*. It is the sounding board of nature and from it the worlds were made. These are deep mysteries but we do know that sound generates vibratory patterns in substance and, through this, forms are created or destroyed and their atomic structures held in place for the period of their manifestation.

The Aether is therefore a vast storehouse of the most immense and immeasurable amounts of energy and the lowest part of this is steadily revealing itself to physicists. When they subtract all the known, measurable energy, forces and matter from space, something very unexpected has been found: rather than it resulting in a vacuum of nothingness, the reverse is the case, with there being almost inconceivably large amounts of energy per cubic centimetre throughout all space. The supposed void seems to have infinity within it, potentially at least. Within it, in the seething cauldron of raw material, are the virtual particles from which actual particles arise.

PD: These ideas about the Big Bang, all these ideas of modern science, modern astronomy – one thing they will not include within their ideas, however far fetched they might seem to be, is that the universe is really permeated by a super-physical consciousness, a consciousness outside the body, a consciousness maybe higher, more profound than that of a human being.

When that is acknowledged then a whole lot of other things about the Earth and our own being will be revealed. While we refuse to acknowledge that we also shut down awareness of the inner worlds and of the Earth itself.

So the paradox is, when we have the right relationship to the cosmos we will then look back at the Earth through this right consciousness as a lens. And we will be able to perceive the deeper realities of the Earth itself.

But that's a stage. You could say we're going through a stage of alienation in our modern physics, in a way necessary if we can get through to the other side. Because we are developing an acuity of vision, an intensity of vision, but we've got to realise that the perceptual organs that they use in technology – what I call the Big Four: the particle collider, electron microscope, radio telescope and mass spectrometer – these are images of perceptual faculties that will arise in human beings in the future – out of the organism.

That's another idea that's not accepted by modern science: that human beings will evolve new faculties. If you do not acknowledge the individual evolution... if you do not acknowledge that – and Darwinian evolutionary theory doesn't, and that's another scientific idea that would be completely modified and transformed by an acknowledgement of the Aetheric – then, if you do not acknowledge that evolution, then everything does, in a way, come to a dead end. And the only possible evolution is purely seen as a technological one, where a human being is replaced or implanted.

LN: So having considered the idea of Aether, how does all this affect us as human beings? What use can we make of this information?

We know from the Chinese and Indian disciplines considered earlier that the conscious appropriation of Aether or Aetheric energy can uplift us and have a healing effect on our mind, body and environment. This is because our own bodies are supported by a scaffold constructed from the Aethers, an Aetheric body that is an exact replica of the gross physical body. Through it, we have access to all the different types of active Aether or *prana* according to our state of consciousness.

It is through the science of mind control, or Rajah Yoga, that we can learn how to assimilate and direct these different currents.

PD: It gives me insights into how to look after my body and my mind. It gives me access to imaginations both in my work as a writer and actor, and enables me to link up thoughts and systems of knowledge, to build bridges in consciousness, to see relationships that normally are not perceived. In some senses it keeps me alive.

The most obvious manifestation of extra-sensory perception is clairvoyance of a certain kind – perceiving the thoughtforms of others.

The other one would be contact with those who have died. And of course, once one acknowledges the Aetheric then it becomes possible to feel these experiences, crossing the threshold.

By acknowledgement of the Aetheric, subtle changes take place in one's organism which almost open doorways, which allow thoughtforms, consciousness, to proceed from the other side into your own being.

If you have a very materialistic consciousness or you just have a built-in denial of these realms, which a lot of people today do, that actually shuts down these doorways in the Aetheric body.

Of course, in the human being, in the physical body we know when a baby is born, the fontanelle is more open, the top of the skull is more open. This closes. This coincides with the shutting out of the memory of where we've come from. So after three years old we really can't contact back. Once we get enclothed in our bodies, the more enclosed we get, we then look out into the physical world, but the other world is closed off from us. We have to go through this intellectual development to establish our individuality, so these realms have to close off temporarily.

In old age often this re-opens. The loosening of the body, the breaking down of this intense holding onto the physical plane – this clutching and grasping together of the skull, the ribs, the whole cohesion of the body which drives away the fluid interaction with the universe – begins to loosen, so that the flowing influx of universal consciousness can flow back into the body. If the body's not prepared for that, or has a life of denying it, then this can manifest as illnesses and disharmonies and dementias and all sorts of other things. If the human being is prepared, then old age can become the first unique experience of the paranormal, a preparation for journeying into those realms. You are actually preparing the journey. You're making the map.

So the first experiences of the paranormal are the chart-creation that will guide you and navigate you through those realms.

The Aetheric realm's the first realm after the physical and the preparation for paranormal experiences is to look at things in the physical world in a new way. For instance, when you look at a tree then you make an effort to see the inner processes. You don't merely see the tree as an object in space. You actually try to enter into the flowing forces within the tree.

With every living thing you take your consciousness a little bit further into the interior dynamics. This will alter your being and will enable then, something to flow back from the non-physical worlds into you at certain moments of time.

LN: Through the Aether, we are all united in the One life. This is the wider purpose of meditation, of linking us all together through the Aetheric medium. On one level we already see this happening through rapid communications systems and the Internet, an outer symbol of the inner developments that are taking place in human consciousness.

We truly live in exciting times – all that the physical sciences have discovered and invented are but mechanical symbols of the capacities that lie deep within us.

The science of meditation provides another means of discovering and wisely using these capabilities.

PD: The acknowledgment of the Aetheric would bring about a fusion between what we call science and art. If the Aether was acknowledged, it would improve and enhance every area of the arts, particularly the plastic arts – sculpture, drawing, painting – and then, of course, theatre, the word, music.

Music is actually the easiest one to understand, because the Aetheric is about rhythm and time, and there are modern composers who have already touched into this. And in a way, the musical world is the least affected by the negative aspects of the non-acknowledgement of the Aetheric. For instance, Philip Glass, Gorecki, people like this, Tippett, these classical composers, have a living experience of the Aetheric. And what I call the minimalistic or process-music as well – you've got this gradual transformation of sound, like a stem growing, gradually moving, subtly changing every moment, coming out of the Aetheric much more a constant flow which gradually changes. Which is also rather like some Oriental music. So that is where the Aetheric manifests more in music.

In the theatre of course, it would be the exploration much more of the cycles of life. I mean, if you're writing a drama, you're going through the different stages of the human being's life and how the consciousness changes as you go through initiations. And also this idea of memory – there are dramas which do explore memory – you know, like flashbacks and recapitulations and living in one's past. The acknowledgement of the Aetheric would really then also lift up, in literature and drama, a much greater understanding of what memory really is.

Acknowledgement of the Aetheric in the arts would open up vistas both of the universe in a completely new way and also give the individual localised human personality a tremendously great context out of which they move and develop and go forward.

Akasha, Internet and Cyberspace

Laurence Newey spoke of 'a plane of manifestation known as the *akasha*'.

The ancient Eastern concepts of *Akasha*, and the *Akashic Record* which refers to a kind of cosmic memory bank, are part of the *consciousness* aspect of the Aether.

Included in this would seem to be what some call the *Platonic* world, a realm of ideal, archetypal forms such as the perfect circle and square - forms which don't exist in physical Nature. It's named after the Greek philosopher, Plato, who lived in a much less materialistic era than ours.

Science is...

Once we realize that *science*, as we normally think of it, is actually the recovery and bringing out into the open of ancient, timeless *occult knowledge*, many things become much clearer. For the word *science* means *knowing* in its broader sense. The key question is how wisely, responsibly and with what motives this is being done, given the inevitable return of the 'exiled' Aether.

The denial of the Aether has been both *explicit* and *implicit*. It's been *explicit* since it was conveniently 'proved' in the 19th century that the Aether doesn't exist... and *implicit* in the way it has been quietly ignored: by science, by organized religion and by the mass media.

This has left a great *gap* and, on either side, the opposed camps – each seeking to create a culture of dependency on its own exclusive expertise.

If we were seeking some kind of 'good' in that denial of the Aether, we could say that there has been an attempt to protect humanity from the danger of getting its hands on something it's not yet mature enough to be trusted with.

On the 'bad' side, however, is the constant temptation – for those who hold at least some of this power knowledge – to keep it to themselves, to indulge their own powerlust, and use it selfishly to gain worldly wealth, prestige and privileges. This touches on some of the darker, occult aspects in relation to the Aether.

In the know

Back in 1991, **Nick Thomas** warned about being aware of developments in aetheric technology. He said: *"If we know what it is all about, the secret brotherhoods won't be able to do much with what they discover. But <u>they</u> would be able to make a great deal of use of something that remained a mystery and about which <u>we</u> knew nothing."*

An example of the power of secret knowledge is perhaps the 1929 Stock Market Crash in the USA which triggered the Great Depression. Just before the Crash, when prices were high, a few individuals, who seemed to know something others didn't, sold large amounts of their investments. After the Crash – which seems not to have been simply an 'accident' – they were then able to buy up huge amounts while prices were extremely low. In this way a few soon became very much richer while millions became poorer. Bearing this example in mind, we may ask, *Who's got 'insider knowledge' about the Aether?*

Free energy?

Arising from ignorance or denial of the Aether is the quest for so-called *free energy* – the idea that Nature can somehow be tricked and exploited – that we can get 'something for nothing'. It's like ignoring the hidden consequences or costs of any activity, whether out of naive unawareness or deliberate self-deception.

Any apparently 'free' physical energy will have been *borrowed* from the aethereal realm. There, certain consequences will ensue and then re-affect the physical realm.

The gap

With physicists now acknowledging that there is no 'empty space', it's realized that there's a gap in their thinking, and various scientific theories have been put forward in attempts to fill this gap. For example, there's the *Zero Point Field, 'dark energy', the Quantum vacuum, morphogenetic fields* – limited glimpses across a turbulent *threshold*. That is, the threshold, known to some as the *edge*, between the *physical* and the *aethereal*.

A powerful affirmation of the Aether has been Ervin Laszlo's proposal of an *Akashic Field*. Yet even his widened horizon still offers a limited view, compromised as it is by the attempt to fit the non-physical, living Aether into the domain of lifeless physics, and then by reverting back to the cosmology of a 'random initial universe' (ie one based on haphazard chance).

But the Aether is <u>not limited</u> and, by its very nature, can't be reduced down to an easy, simple definition. So we approach it in this project from a range of angles and levels, and in this way build up a fuller impression of it.

Professor of Biology, **Brian Goodwin** – formerly with the Open University – is a very independent-minded thinker, writer and teacher.

A Biologist's View of the Aether
Brian Goodwin

Well, I'm a biologist and I started my career in Canada with a Biology degree. I was never very happy with the way biology was taught because it seemed the dominant way of looking at evolution was Darwinism and whereas certain aspects of

Darwin's thinking are quite brilliant and clearly exceedingly useful, it also has its limitations. And it was the limitations I was very much aware of. And I think the limitations that I experience in biology are directly related to this concept of the Aether because it's the context of the parts that I've always been interested in – in trying to understand the whole.

And the most obvious whole in biology is the whole organism. But there are many other wholes; a beehive is a whole – it's an integral totality that is coherent. Ecosystems, microbial communities – these are wholes in the sense that they don't have a very well-defined boundary but they have a coherence about them. So what fascinates me is, how are we to understand those wholes and their properties? Because the properties are not simply quantities. It's the qualitative interaction, it's the quality of life that they have. So those are all properties of the whole.
Well, in biology there isn't really a language for talking about wholes.

Science has tried to, effectively, get rid of the notion of life from matter. And if there's no life in matter then how on earth do they think that organisms come about? 'Matter' and 'mother' are the same root. Now 'matter', as we have developed it in science, has no qualities that you would associate with 'mother'. None. Those have all been expurgated from the concept of matter.

And of course the conventional view that I was brought up with was the idea that you got a whole lot of mechanical interactions between component parts – the molecules at one level, molecules, ions, electrical currents in nerves and various types of mechanical and chemical activity are going on. You've got a whole constellation of these, which biologists have been busy cataloguing. It's like elementary particle physics: there's

31

no end to particles if you want to look at things from that point of view. It's endless. It's the same with biology. It will be endless – the constellation of molecules, the cataloguing can go on and on for ever. So at some point you have to say, how do these things work together?

So this is the whole, the dynamic of the whole being, and if you extend that through from atoms, molecules, cells, organisms, communities, Gaia...(I'll come back to that because it is a concept that has come back from Hesiod, from 8th century Greece, this concept of the Earth). The Earth is itself an expression of the Aether, if I use the term to say: every time we're talking about a whole, an integral, coherent whole, we're talking about some sort of – for want of a better word I'll use the term – a matrix or binding quality that gives that set of separately identifiable components their coherence, their wholeness.

And of course the term that is used in science for this, the technical term, is 'a field'. Now that's a pretty neutral term. But it's absolutely filled with mystery. The concept of 'field' has been filled with mystery right from the beginning in science. And it's this quality of mystery which, of course, is the intriguing thing about the Aether. Again, we never come to the end of the mysteries of Aether.

And if you're talking about a binding matrix, you're talking about 'anima mundi' or the 'soul of the world' ('anima' in Latin means soul). And so we have this idea that animate Earth is a recognition that the Earth has a soul, and the soul of the earth is an expression of the Aether.... in this particular terrestrial form.

As a biologist, and a biologist with training in mathematics, I have tried to articulate this notion of 'field' in biology as the coherent context for the expression of the properties of living systems.

How is it they come to be? You start with a single cell – let's say the egg of the frog. It gets fertilised and that spherical object turns into this amazing being, the frog. How does that happen? Well, that is an expression of the Aether. But it's Aether animated in a particular way in the context of life.

I mean, Aether is animated in different ways in different contexts. In some sense all these different contexts are continuous with one another; they're part of the same expression of the soul. And the soul is this continuous mystery. But intuitively we know what we mean by the soul. It's a term we don't use any more in science but it has now come back in the language that we use within what we call wholistic science which is focused on trying to understand the emergent properties of wholes. And these are whole organisms, whole communities (and that includes human communities), whole ecosystems, the whole earth. We go as far as the whole cosmos, but not in any systematic sense. We don't try to be astrophysicists and talk about Big Bangs and so on and so forth.

I do believe – and this is something that, for me, comes from Goethe – the whole exists always at the same time as the parts. You don't get parts coming together to make wholes. The whole exists with the parts. It's the way Goethe did his science, and many other people. We use Goethe as a historical example from within the Western tradition because he was both a scientist and a poet and an administrator. He had all these skills.

So, what we call wholistic science is the same as wholistic living; it's learning the skills for quality of life, quality of community.

Communities are where the action has to be in order for us to finally get a decent semblance of democracy – we don't have any democracy really – and that will give rise to new patterns of governance and new constellations. I've no idea what they're going to be, except they're all going to be self-organised anarchic structures.

Now anarchism is not a word that sits easily in most people's ears, but there's a sense in which anarchy is precisely the traditional type of governance for self-organising, emergent, complex interactive systems of the type we've been talking about. But there won't be one form of governance, there'll be many. And that's the healthy thing. This is the way to reach meaning for human culture.

It's going to be tough work but it's going to be so joyful. And it's going to be such fun. And it's going to be so grounding that I just think it's a fantastic time to be alive. It's a tough time to be alive but at the same time it is full of opportunity and potential for transformation. So, I can't think of a better time to be around than the early 21st century.

The anarchism Brian Goodwin refers to would seem to imply a freedom and diversity of expression within a sense of the greater unity which he acknowledges as the Aether.

Beings and corpses

Since the *Aether* has the inherent quality of *aliveness*, it must itself be some kind of living entity, a *being*. Perhaps we can relate to this notion in the way that we think of, say, a *city* having a living identity, a life of its own. For a city includes many individual lives and also manifests in material objects, such as buildings, roads and other things.

And as *human beings*, the 'being' aspect of us is our aliveness and consciousness, as opposed to the disintegrating matter of which our physical bodies are formed. For what we call the human body wouldn't actually exist without its vital background *aethereal* component animating its functioning.

The opposite of *life* is, of course, *death*. And *matter*, put simply, is dead stuff.

It's solidified, congealed *energy* or *life*, trapped in physical form.

MW: **The whole of physical science, as we can see, is dealing with corpses – and the corpse of the aetheric energy. That's the beginning and the end of it. That is the root of the whole business.**

That's scientist and engineer, **Michael Watson**.

Physics is...

Physics is a misleading name. The word *Physics* itself was coined relatively recently, from an ancient Greek word which means living, growing *Nature*. And that's where the much older word *physician*, meaning natural healer or doctor, comes from.

Physics is today still assumed to be the foundation of all the other sciences which supposedly can be reduced down to Physics. In other words, it's claimed that all Biology can be reduced down to Chemistry, and all Chemistry can be reduced down to the so-called 'laws' of Physics.

Now, *Physics* is officially the study of *matter, energy* and *forces*. And Albert Einstein, stated that *matter* is *energy*. Yet, according to another highly acclaimed 20th century physicist, **Richard Feynman**: *'Science fails to admit that it has not the slightest clue what energy is.'*

Then, in a BBC radio tribute to Einstein in 2005, UK physicist Brian Cox admitted that, a hundred years on, Western science still doesn't know what *mass* or *matter* actually is. And elsewhere in this project, Professor of Physics, **Ian J Thompson** states that physicists don't really understand the concept of *force* either.

Even Newton's so-called First Law, on motion and force, explains nothing about what *force* is, and turns out to be a self-referencing, circular description – what's known as a *tautology*.

And further, as indicated later in this project, there is now the view that Einstein's famous $E = mc^2$ is ill-founded – although it does point towards a deep truth about matter and energy.

Nick Thomas, himself an electrical engineer, has said that we don't really know what *electricity* is, although we're familiar with and cleverly exploit certain natural phenomena we call electricity and electromagnetism.

Now, physics is promoted as a soundly constructed discipline. But based on these very dubious foundations, it begins to look more like a set of hopeful, speculative beliefs.

NT: As from the early 1930s, when they had the Copenhagen meeting and came to the conclusion that Physics cannot explain anything, Physics can only calculate the probability of how experiments will turn out. But it cannot explain them and will not try.

However, we can see the apparently bizarre and irrational findings of Quantum Physics making some sense when looked at as a kind of *visionary revelation* – unintentional, of course. For it does link our present day micro-detailed awareness with the ancient wisdom-knowing of humanity, mostly ignored in the Western world for the last few hundred years. And this is the view we gain from the *threshold* of the *physical* and the *aethereal*.

Shut up and calculate

When one vital, essential factor is written out of a culture, removed from the equation and thus from our thinking, all our other ideas and concepts become distorted and compromised, in our attempt to compensate for that missing element. Then, starting out with false assumptions, we inevitably end up with wrong conclusions – which, sadly, has been the case with Western science.

Its version of science has become limited to enquiring *'What does what in what particular circumstances?'* and *'How can it be measured and quantified?'*

Thus the infamous instruction given to some modern physics students, referred to here by Professor of Physics, **Ian Thompson**:

ITh: **The Copenhagen Interpretation is sometimes called the 'Shut up and Calculate' approach. It tells us to calculate but doesn't allow us to ask questions.**

The following quoted excerpt from Harvard Professor of Genetics, **Richard Lewontin**, eloquently highlights one of the main self-inflicted problems of Western science.

> *'We take the side of science in spite of the patent absurdity of some of its constructs, in spite of its failure to fulfill many of its extravagant promises of health and life, in spite of the tolerance of the scientific community for unsubstantiated 'Just So' stories, because we have a prior commitment, a commitment to materialism...'*

And that's about as clear an admission as it could be of prejudice in Western science. Further on, Lewontin, in his frank and honest way, says:

> *'It is not the truth that makes you free. It is your possession of the power to discover the truth. Our dilemma is that we do not know how to provide that power.'*

The response to this is that Western science needs to evolve beyond its own dogma and denial and once more become a source of inspiration.

In June 2005, BBC News referred to physics and chemistry as being 'in terminal decline'. This was based on the diminishing student demand for courses in physics and chemistry, with the result that university departments are having to close down.

The Engineer's Report that follows is a brief but penetrating investigation into the troubling question: 'What's missing that makes science such a turn-off?'

The Report is based mainly on a series of talks and consultative dialogues conducted by engineer and scientist, **Nick Thomas**. Nick has significantly advanced the mathematics of projective geometry, and has written on the philosophy of science. Significantly, he has also studied and written about Goethe's classic drama, *Faust*, the character who traded his soul for the promise of worldly power and reaped the dire consequences.

Because his availability for recording was limited, some of Nick's thoughts are conveyed by the narrators of this Report.

What's missing that makes science such a turn-off?

Engineer's Report 2006

On the current predicament of Western science

With contributions from

N C Thomas MIEE

and

Dr Edi Bilimoria

Dr Margaret Colquhoun

Professor Brian Goodwin

David Lorimer

Professor Ian J Thompson

Michael Watson MIEE

Professor Arthur Zajonc

CONTENTS

WHY AN ENGINEER'S REPORT?

The Predicament

1   Western Science is now widely felt to be inaccessible, out of control, suspicious and even sinister – rather than an admirable or attractive pursuit.

2   Scientists are now mistrusted because they are seen as lacking in integrity and driven by greed, personal ambition and commercial interests.

3   Science has become an unappealing subject to study, felt to be cold and sterile, despite attempts to make it seem more interesting and exciting.

4   The human species, the natural world and the planet are becoming increasingly unhealthy, polluted and endangered, despite the many so called advances in science and technology.

The Purpose

1   To identify the deeper causes of the predicament behind the superficial symptoms blighting Western science.

2   To propose practical remedies, both general and specific, in order to achieve and maintain its optimum functioning.

3   Free from any constraints of sponsorship or other partisan interests, to be broad in range, leaving detailed coverage for later follow-ups.

Why an Engineer?

The engineer has to know how to harness the forces and substances of nature, subtle and gross, in order to achieve specific, desired results.

The engineer is the most practical of scientists and technologists, and includes the roles of inventor, designer and troubleshooter.

The engineer assesses whether a system (a) is based on *sound principles*, (b) is *elegant* in *design* and (c) *works efficiently*.

The engineer does not confuse the theory, the blueprint or the model with the real world, nor the map with the territory.

Preview

NT: Right now we've gained so much power, scientific power.

As we know, we have the power to destroy the Earth if we're stupid enough to do so.

We have the power now, as we dive into the genome, to interfere with life itself. And we're going to do all of that on inadequate knowledge, because... I think the Aether is an integral and vital part of all of that.

The Engineer's Report on the current predicament of Western science.

The investigating engineer has to be both scientist and detective. It's the scientist who distinguishes between unquestioned dogma or superstition... and *testable truths*, and it's the detective who seeks out the *motives* behind actions. And an engineer is more likely to detect a deliberately engineered situation where others might see only randomness.

This will not be a comfortable journey.

Questions will arise which will inevitably lead to some deeply challenging conclusions which some people may find discomforting.

Over a few hundred years the inconsistent mass of theory and practice generally labeled 'science' has become an integral part of Western, and now, world culture.

We do need to bear in mind that the label 'science' covers a wide range of activities. First there's the official, state approved, orthodox science, as taught in schools, colleges and universities. Then there's a wealth of unorthodox science being pursued by various individuals and companies for all kinds of motives – some generally beneficial to the world, and some harmful. There is also the darker, secret science of which the general public is largely kept in ignorance.

NT: We've arrived at a situation where we have a world outlook which has led, as we have seen, to certain ways of thinking about agriculture, certain ways of thinking about medicine, certain ways of thinking about education, all of which we're finding are problematic.

Nick Thomas, engineer, scientist and mathematician,

How do we deal with GM food? Nobody knows how to think about it. Because the missing ingredient in all of these things is the Aether.

It's the Aether that gives us life. It's the Aether that gives us vitality. It's the Aether that makes us healthy or ill. Or at least, it has a huge role to play in all of that. And if we have no idea what the Aether is then obviously we're going to judge these things in a false way.

Engineers have to be the most practical of scientists – and especially so when investigating a malfunctioning system and assessing how its failings may best be remedied. Then, it's essential to find the causes which underlie the superficial symptoms, as well as, vitally, the missing ingredient referred to by Nick Thomas.

And to take a practical, professional look at the failings of Western science as a whole, the engineer needs to see it in a greater context – historical, social-political, ecological and cosmic.

In this respect, taking an overview also helps detect patterns not apparent from ground level.

As a responsible, straight talking engineer-scientist of some forty years experience, Nick Thomas will not play along with any psychological games of denial regarding science – since for him this would amount to 'living a lie'. And it would be a profoundly unscientific way to proceed.

'Denial' here refers to Western science's continuing denial-by-omission of the Aether – which has required it to come up with all manner of complicated distortions and fabrications in order to fill or conceal the great gaps left. The result is a confused tangle of paradoxes, contradictions, taboos and dogma.

These unfortunately devalue the positive achievements of Western science, which only concerns itself with physical phenomena. All the more so when it then over-extends its capabilities, when it tries, quite inappropriately, to address levels of reality it's neither competent nor equipped to handle. Which inevitably leads to false conclusions and wrong actions, sometimes with dire consequences.

Also, to be denied vital knowledge is to be disempowered. And when people are taught that something they need to know about doesn't even exist then we have a double denial.

And it's clear that this message, repeated to students and trainee teachers through generations, results in it eventually becoming accepted fact – all the more so when serious and deep questioning is neither taught nor encouraged, but is rather seen as trouble-making and not at all good for your career prospects.

DL: Presuppositions or philosphical assumptions that underlie the teaching of science and medicine are not stated. They're implied. And they're assumed by the teachers. And so the teachers pass it on uncritically.

David Lorimer: teacher, writer and Programme Director of the Scientific and Medical Network, talking here with Nick Thomas.

And so the students then receive this understanding uncritically as well, because nobody asks them whether this is actually a complete understanding.

NT: That's right. They don't even almost know there's a question to ask the teachers. I mean, I had that – when I left school I read a book which gave a completely different picture of science from all that I'd been taught, and I fought every page of it. But in so doing, realised how I'd been brainwashed without knowing it.

When one asks, How is that status quo sustained? Why is one up against hostility? Why is one up against strong resistance? – of course, it's a very mixed picture. There's an awful a lot of ingredients there. You have everything, from people who have a position to maintain – they have an academic position or academic respectability, they are committed to a paradigm and they don't want to be budged from it, their whole life, their whole work, their whole reputation depend upon it – they're the last people to want to see something brand new swept in.

Thomas Kuhn, who studied this whole issue of, how do great changes come about in scientific thinking – he was the one who coined this term, 'paradigm' – what he said was, when one has a sweeping change come about in people's outlook, what he called a 'paradigm change', that sweeping change is brought about by young people because they don't have reputations they're protecting.

Very often, really new ideas come about through amateurs, so-called. Very often a professional person is so blinkered in their profession that they're unable to see outside, something brand new.

The purpose of this Report is not to criticize individuals or groups. It is to identify where and how scientists are failing humanity, and how we can rethink and remedy the situation.

Scientists are seen here not as a species apart, operating in a no-go area, but as normal, fallible human beings. And this includes the exceptionally gifted ones too, such as Newton, Darwin and Einstein – as we'll see later. For there is great danger when science is allowed to become a separate, 'value-free', ie *no responsibility*, zone, obligated only to its paymasters or sponsors, and unaccountable to the rest of humanity.

A stark example would be the case of the early Quantum physicists in America in the context of the Second World War. They were tempted, hired and then manipulated by the military and other, more powerful influences... while working in a secret location, mostly isolated from the everyday world of ordinary people, with whom they were forbidden to discuss their work... at any time.

So today it's everybody's business to know what's being done on their behalf in the name of science – whether in weaponry, medicine, genetic engineering, nano-technology or whatever else.

Consequently this *Report* will not be a mere academic, intellectual exercise. It will simply say what needs to be said, and not collude in any denial or deception.

Historically, Western science emerged out of a defiant opposition to the then dominating, corrupt and dogmatic, multi-national Church organization.

And it defended itself by adopting a polar opposite stance which sadly, over time, has crystallized and rigidified into a distorted mirror image of the institution it was opposing.

Now, a few hundred years on, the leaderships of both sides have a mutual interest in prolonging the battle. But it's the scientists who seem more threatened, as *Aether* awareness arises again.

That's because they've become weakened through boxing themselves in, through narrowing their outlook and limiting their scope for inspiration.

NT: **It's getting to the point now where eyes have been closed when they should be open. Things have been denied – like, for instance, the experiments of Benveniste over homeopathy – these sort of things.**

    I mean, they are desperate not to acknowledge any truth to such a result. Now that shows anti-science, not science.

Neuroscientist, **Professor Candace Pert**, is the author of the acclaimed book *Molecules of Emotion*. In it she describes how *winning* is 'the fuel that feeds the modern science machine', and being first to publish is 'the big pay off', even if you have to 'play dirty'.

In the history of ideas and the growth of human knowledge Western science appears like a small boy – highly motivated by an ethos of rivalry and competition, and indulging in heroic fantasies of adventure, conquests and cures. It has been fascinated by extremes such as the biggest, smallest, loudest, strongest and fastest.

Like most boys, Western science has tended to admire cleverness and force. It has sought outer, physical results and become obsessed by numbers and quantities at the expense of qualities and experience.

Two fairly recent examples of this have been the races to be first with: (a) a vaccine for HIV/AIDS and (b) the so-called complete human genome – with all the falsifying and short cuts it took to 'win' at all costs.

And from the attempt to rationalize this attitude a motto has emerged:
'Science is value free'. In other words, a scientist is not responsible for the consequences of the science he carries out.

Perhaps the epitome of this trivialising attitude came in a BBC radio science discussion, from a British Professor of Genetics when he said: "Ethics is to science what pornography is to sex..."

Western medicine has been and still is diligently following wherever Western science leads it. Dazzled and seduced by technical cleverness, it has lost touch with the sense of *wholeness* that characterises *healing*.

Convinced that matter comes before consciousness, it focusses on fixing symptoms, as if the human being were little more than a complex machine. And with today's rapid advances in micro-biological techniques, the dangers of applying that mechanistic mindset to the living world are greatly increased.

Meanwhile, the religious fundamentalists know how humans yearn for some deeper, higher meaning in their lives – however simplistic – and become disillusioned with the prospect of a soulless, spiritless world.

There is significance in the timing of this Report. The power of the *Aether* is of a scale way beyond our normal human capacity to comprehend. However, that has never stopped certain people trying to grasp it – for all manner of motives, good and evil.

There is, then, considerable risk in raising public awareness of the *Aether*. But, for an engineer familiar with risk assessment, it now seems clear that the dangers of irresponsible misuse are outweighed by the perils of leaving this powerful knowledge in the hands of a few – to exploit for their own purposes.

NT: **You have a technology at your fingertips which can be used for good or evil. Because it depends upon you as a personality. Therefore there's more involved than the Aether. One of the aspects of that is that your feelings are also involved, which are not Aetheric – they're above the Aether.**

       If you know how to bring forces to bear to make somebody better, you also know how to bring forces to bear to make them worse. It's always two-edged. And the Aether is no exception to that.

The problems of Western science seem to have arisen primarily from it having been corrupted by the belief system known as *materialism*. This proclaims that *matter* is the ultimate reality – despite physics simultaneously stating that matter is actually condensed *energy*, while energy itself remains a deep mystery.

Consciousness, meanwhile, is the ultimate mystery for materialistic science – its Holy Grail, some would say. Materialism portrays the emergence of matter from consciousness in reverse, ending up with a picture of a haphazard, meaningless, fragmented universe.

The Aether can serve as a connecting stage to higher levels of being, if that's what's being sought. *Aether awareness* is not some kind of ultimate body of knowledge. What it does is extend and clarify our experiences, setting them in a greater context, enhancing every area of our lives.

However, don't expect to find this view being presented in a balanced way by any mass media corporations or by any orthodox science journals. The reasons for this merit some thinking about.

NT: Are we into Conspiracy Theory? Are we saying that somewhere or other somebody is manipulating the strings? And I have to say that, to some degree, the answer's, Yes.

I'm not a conspiracy theorist. I'm always suspicious of conspiracy theorists, largely because when you get sucked into Conspiracy Theory it's like putting on a pair of red glasses – everything looks red. When you put your Conspiracy Theory glasses on, everything is a conspiracy.

On the other hand, it's obvious there are conspiracies. And what one then comes to is, What kind of forces lie behind our life?

We know there are forces that lie behind our life for the good, and there are also forces that lie behind our life for evil. And if one becomes conscious of where and how those kinds of forces are active, then one can rise to whatever level one's capable of in trying to meet it.

And since there's no discernible level at which all this ceases to be relevant, the questions remain open-ended.

NT: I do think that Aether awareness is actually against certain special interests which are, at a very high level, manipulating to some degree, human beings. So yes, I think that's definitely so.

How high does one go in trying to meet that? One has to go to whatever height one's own abilities permit. And the first step in doing so is to be willing to pursue this kind of work and pursue elaborating the thoughts which go against those special interests. And one goes as high as one can in doing that.

Still taught as science today, also, is the fallacious idea that the existence of the Aether has been conclusively disproved. This is about as unscientific as claiming that, since the latest high-tech telescopes have searched the skies and found no white-bearded old man, no superhuman life exists. Case proved, no further questions necessary.

In this project we've adopted an open-ended rather than a closed approach.

First, in this Report, we'll briefly outline three essential ingredients for achieving our purpose: the *Aether* itself, followed by the two fundamental principles, *Wholeness* and *Polarity*, which together form a necessary part of any wholistic and balanced attitude to scientific work.

Then we'll look at a few key areas in current science. And to each of these we'll apply three basic engineering tests, asking:

> **- Is the thinking based on sound principles?**
> **- Is the science in question elegant in design?**
> **- Does the system or theory operate efficiently?**

David Lorimer again,

DL: Scientists act as philosophers; they say philosophical things. And you cannot divorce science from its metaphysical context because if you don't make your philosophy explicit then it's going to remain implicit. Because you cannot exist without having a set of assumptions which you operate from.

Metaphysics means 'beyond physics' and is defined in Chambers dictionary as 'the science which investigates first principles of nature and thought'.

Meanwhile, there is one crucial distinction of which a responsible, thinking engineer will be aware. And it's between, first, the many clever, ingenious technologies, ie the know-how to make particular things happen or prevent them... and second, a clear understanding of the universal principles behind living Nature and the cosmos... which would amount to a true, mature science, willing to take responsibility for the consequences of its actions.

In July 2006 on BBC radio, Emeritus Professor of History of Science, Colin Morris, pointed out how a wide range of historians today regard materialistic Western science as a direct product of Christian theology amongst other influences – somewhat to the surprise of the presenter, Dr Brian Cox, a physicist.

At the beginning of each section we'll openly state our startout *assumptions* and our *key question* on the subject.

And at all times we'll need to be aware that the language we use to describe the world we experience through our *physical* senses is quite inadequate for describing the qualities of the *aethereal* realm – which we do experience, but in a very different way.

The Aether

EB: Are we saying that it's indispensible that we understand the Aether and work with it?

Dr Edi Bilimoria: consultant engineer on such high profile projects as the Channel Tunnel and London Underground, speaking here with Nick Thomas:

NT: Yes, I believe so, for several reasons. First of all, we're desperately going to need it. Our current technological resources will run out, I think. I mean, it's obvious, even if it's hundreds of years, sooner or later those current resources will run out and we're going to need something else.

        Secondly, people are evolving, and as people change they're going to start demanding another kind of technology, because they will feel that current technology is somehow... that there's something wrong with it.

EB: It's polluting.

NT: Right. And people speak about nuclear power stations, I think fancifully, but they speak about them as 'black altars' and things like this. Well, I think that's going too far, but I know where they're coming from, you know? And this is going to get much stronger in the next few hundred years.

EB: Because the energy you spend in dis-assembling it is far more than what you get out of it.

NT: Exactly. And that's another long story. But that's one very important reason why we need to work with this whole conception of the Aether. Secondly, we're not going to solve fundamental problems unless we grasp the background of what's going on around us properly. We haven't done so, so far. Whereas if you understand what's really happening then you're not doing all that damage.

First, the

ENGINEER'S ASSUMPTION

Instinct, intellect and intuition all tell us that there's much more to our experience of being human than merely physical phenomena and their effects. And we can learn to recognise the *Aether* in our experiencing of its own special qualities, which are quite distinct from what we sense *physically*.

KEY QUESTION – Since the *Aether* can't be sensed physically and can't be summed up in a neat definition, how can we build up an impression of it?

NT: One starts with the simplest experience we have of all – which is that we're alive. It's the most patently obvious fact to everybody.

And of course one doesn't then want to try and explain life away as something else, because life is life. That's the starting point. Something as straightforward as life is obviously in itself wholistic. It's organic in its whole quality. And so Aether begins there.

So one immediately grasps Aether as that sort of informing wholistic principle.

OVERVIEW

Awareness of the *Aether* is what's crucially missing from our present Western science and culture. And this 'absence' is at the heart and root of many of our problems, great and small.

NT: Now a lot of people fall into the sort of habit of thinking, Oh yes, well on the one hand we have matter, and on the other hand we have this mysterious 'whatever it is'....

EB: Spirit, so called.

NT: ....Yes, whatever it is that makes wholism, but 'never the twain shall meet.' Now, I'm an engineer, and I want to know what the levers and pulleys are that connect the two together. If Aether's important, if Aether actually exists, as I believe it does, then it must make a difference to something.

If it doesn't make a difference to anything then why have it?

And I think it's just those differences that are why we need the Aether.

EB: And one would go further and say, it's not just a hypothesis we postulate to fill a hole. It is a very real thing.

Here's biology professor, **Brian Goodwin's** view of the Aether.

BG: I think the limitations that I experience in Biology are directly related to this concept of the Aether, because it's the context of the parts that I've always been interested in, in trying to understand the whole.

In the emerging of this universe from a state of *oneness* or *singularity*, the *Aether* can be thought of as an intermediate, *pre-physical* stage in that momentous cosmic process. As such, it continues to function 'behind' the outer physical world, exerting a subtle but powerful influence on all things physical.

So we <u>are</u> very much aware of it, once we know what 'it' is. And we <u>do</u> experience its qualities, but not directly through our physical senses. We infer its continuous presence from its outer physical effects.

Water, a *liquid*, cannot be understood in terms of solid matter such as wood. Yet radiating wave patterns can be detected frozen in the *grain* of wood, providing a snapshot of the growth process.

And we note that Aether is not a finer kind of physical substance, like a more subtle version of air, but is of a wholly different order of existence, functioning according to different principles.

NT: It's actually a direct apprehension, if I can put it in a most general way, of a dimension of reality that simply is not describable by our physical processes.

Sir Isaac Newton knew and wrote about the *Aether* and about a universal expansive force which used to be known as *Levity*, and is the complementary opposite of *Gravity*. *Gravity* and *Levity* are the two polar forces of the *Aether*, and thus of the universe.

EB: Newton's works contain a tremendous amount of insight into the Aether.

He was always trying to identify what he called two 'sperms' or two forces. One was the inward-seeking, contracting force – he called that Gravity. The other one was what's known as the expanding force in Newton's cosmos. Now what he said is, that expanding force operates not only in light but also in chemicals – in chemical compositions – and also in biology, and in the minds of animals and man.

So maybe he was really using different terms – and this is the problem – maybe he was always alluding to this Aether Principle.

In the 19th century, science in the United Kingdom, the leading industrial country, represented the classic age of machine-minded thinking. Scientists then, tried to identify a subtle but material aether as the medium through which electromagnetic light waves travel.

But the quest to establish this kind of aether failed and the whole notion of an aether was abandoned within orthodox science.

NT: At the end of the nineteenth century one of the huge problems they had was, they imagined this imponderable Aether that was perfectly elastic, perfectly this, perfectly that – an absurdity in the end.

EB: It had to be infinitely elastic and yet infinitely stiff.

NT: Exactly

EB: And they just couldn't have both. They were again looking at it as a mechanical Aether, and what knocked out the mechanical Aether, of course, was the famous Michelson-Morley experiments.

NT: According to some interpretations.

EB: According to some. There were other Michelson-Morley experiments that were performed that gave very doubtful results, dubious results.

And some actually confirm the existence of an Aether. All these anomalous Michelson-Morley experiments have been reported in Nature, New Scientist, and learned journals.

NT: The point about the Michelson-Morley experiment being, of course, is that sometimes it's seen as a conclusive proof that there is no Aether, or that Relativity is correct.

But it's based upon quite a number of assumptions, and one has to careful not to see it as the rock-solid piece of experimental evidence that it is supposed to be. An experiment is always interpreted according to presumptions, assumptions, or to use the more modern term, a paradigm. And it depends what assumption you make as to how you interpret that experiment.

So it was thought for instance that Light has a velocity, and it's travelling through a medium – namely the 'Ether' – and the attempt was then made to measure the speed of the Earth relative to this Ether. That's what Michelson and Morley wanted to do. And it was a very sensitive experiment. As far as we know it was sensitive enough to indicate what they wanted it to, but they got a null result.

So that left several possibilities. No Ether, was one possibility. Another one was that somehow the Earth was dragging the Ether with it and therefore no difference was seen. There were a number of different interpretations possible. So it's not a conclusive experiment as is sometimes thought.

And above all, it's based on assumptions which are not necessarily correct – the major one, I think, being the assumption that Light has a definite velocity and is travelling at a definite velocity through space. And as we'll see later, that's an assumption that can well be challenged on the basis of a new concept of the Aether.

Max Planck, a leading professor of physics at that time, and founding father of Quantum Physics, said:

> "If we wish to arrive at a concept of what we call Aether nowadays, the first requirement is to follow the only path open to us in view of the knowledge of modern physics, and consider the Aether non-material."

Einstein, in 1920, explicitly affirmed the existence of the Aether.

EB: Einstein never threw out the Aether. I have an actual facsimile of a lecture he gave to senior students at the University of Leyden in the Netherlands. And he said, There is nothing in Relativity that discards an Aether.

What it does discard are these absurd notions of the Victorian Ether. But not the idea of an Aether *per se*.

Now there are numerous signs of the Aether being acknowledged again under various other names such as dark energy.

I Th: The idea of such a background substance in the world still comes up in physics.

Ian Thompson, Professor of Physics at the University of Surrey, England, speaking of the mysterious dark energy and dark matter.

I don't know if you've heard a lot about 'dark matter' in astronomy these days. Apparently about 60% or 80% of the universe is composed of 'dark matter'.

Back with **Edi Bilimoria** and **Nick Thomas**,

EB: First astronomers postulated 'dark matter', but now they've moved considerably further and they are reinstating Einstein's cosmological constant.

Einstein put in a cosmological constant to render his equations static because he then thought the Universe was static – his biggest blunder. But now they're finding that cosmological constant is the basis of what a lot of physicists and top astronomers are calling, 'the basis of an Aethereal energy diffused through all space'.......

NT: Yes, it's 'dark energy'

EB: Well, more than that. They're saying that it stands on its own feet almost, so to speak, that without that aethereal energy we just wouldn't be here, and the planets wouldn't be here, and so on.

I Th: There's another kind of process in physics which has often also been identified with Aether. And this is the idea of 'zero point motion' – the fact that in a vacuum there are many things which appear to be happening or potentially happening, but not actually happening. And so there's this idea of 'zero point motion' or 'zero point energy', which is the energy in the vacuum. And this has often been thought of as the Aether. Is it just vacuum?

NT: No, I think there's much more to it than that. I'm coming to the view that 'zero point action', if you like, if one can call it that, the actions that are going on – particles popping into existence and vanishing again – that is actually an interface. It isn't the Aether, but it's an interface between the physical and the Aether.

Roger Penrose, a current leading physicist and mathematician, has spoken of a 'missing physics' needed to handle the elusive subject of *consciousness*.

This is what he said in a recent broadcast:

(His words are spoken by an actor)

RP: I think the major revolution, which I do think we need, would involve a complete re-thinking of, not just Quantum Mechanics, but how we look at Space and Time and all sorts of things. So, there'll be a revolution waiting in the wings. And when that revolution has come, OK, maybe then we can think about issues like, What thought is. I mean, what is it? I mean,

61

in my view, conscious thinking <u>does</u> depend on this unknown part of physics.

The Aether, in its interaction with the *physical* realm, creates the conditions within which consciousness becomes possible. But it is not itself *physical*, and is thus beyond the scope of Physics. It is the missing stage or level between the higher, subtle, cosmic, spiritual realm and the lower, coarse, earthly, material realm.

On BBC Radio 4's *In Our Time*, **Melvyn Bragg** challenged leading American physicist, **Professor Brian Greene**, and UK Astronomer Royal, **Sir Martin Rees**, with the unavoidable question about 'the missing Physics':

(His words are spoken by an actor)

MB: **What you're saying is, there's this huge theory, which gently warps the fabric of the Universe. But it is <u>built</u> on the particles, the 'quarks', at the bottom, a theory which has got nothing to do with the huge theory. So ordinary Joes would say, Why don't the building blocks lead to the building?**

When we talk about 'the missing physics', we mean – we've got the little, we've got the big. So we need something in between to link them together.

Brian Greene said 'We need a bridge between them.' Martin Rees agreed.

Nick Thomas has for many years been referring to his work as 'building the necessary bridge' – and in two senses at once. First, to provide the missing connection between the micro and macro worlds, which so far Western science has been unable to unite. And second, to enable minds to span the apparent gap between consciousness and matter, or the cosmic and the earthly.

NT: One must try and build a bridge. One wants to meet one's
        fellow human beings. Every single human being, even if that
        person is a rigid, materialistic, orthodox scientist, is still a
        human being, and actually has an Aether-body, even if they
        don't agree with you.

        And they actually have, deep in their soul, a knowledge of the
        truth, even if it's been covered over by education and by
        upbringing and so on. And so one always retains that faith that
        one can reach the core of every human being somehow.

        And so one's going to try to build a bridge to people without,
        however, abdication. Without seeking approval in the wrong
        sense.

        The way I'm trying to approach it is to build this bridge
        between what seem like two worlds of our ordinary
        consciousness. And I'm beginning with Projective Geometry as
        a very useful method for building that bridge. Because I think
        that is a bridge whereby our scientific friends of today who
        cannot or will not grasp the more subtle aspects.... it is a
        bridge they could cross if they have the goodwill.

Mathematics is a way of thinking not limited by the
constraints of physical nature. It's a language, a code, rooted
at its deepest level in *rhythm*. Now rhythm is ultimately
about *time*, time prior to *physical space* and the formation of
matter. And the pre-physical state of the cosmos is as
Aether. Numbers, being essentially abstract ideas, are thus
aethereal and of the realm of unlimited possibilities or
potential. As such, they can be manipulated to produce just
about any result that is desired. An obvious example is in
the use of statistics.

So, making the necessary jump in thinking from 'physics-is-
the-whole—story' to a broader science of the Aether would

effectively be the 'revolution' which Penrose predicts and awaits.

Within its wholeness and inherent polarity, the *Aether* can be seen to consist of four distinct grades or qualities. These are known as the *Warmth Aether*, the *Light Aether*, the *Tone or Chemical Aether* and the *Life Aether*.

They correspond to the four traditional elements, known as *Fire, Air, Water* and *Earth*.

THE ENGINEER'S 3 TESTS

- regarding Western science and the Aether

TEST 1: SOUND PRINCIPLES?

To an engineer, Western science's attitude of, 'a material aether or no aether at all' is <u>not</u> a sound startout principle. For the old materialistic, machine-minded worldview has long been superceded, on the one hand by *Quantum Physics* (even with all its anomalies and paradoxes) and on the other by the subtle but profound implications of *Chaos Theory*.

NT: There are two things which I think have been of enormous importance in the last fifty to one hundred years. One of them being the discoveries in Quantum Physics which you've just been talking about. As from the early 1930s, when they had the Copenhagen meeting and came to the conclusion that Physics cannot explain anything. Physics can only calculate the probability of how experiments will turn out. It cannot explain and will not try.

The other thing is the discovery of Chaos Theory – the discovery that there are systems which are so sensitive that they are, in principle, non-predictable.

TEST 2: ELEGANT DESIGN?

Presently Western science offers only an inelegant patchwork of stop-gap theories and models in its attempt to fill the great gaps resulting from the denial of the Aether. Among these are the *Zero Point Field*, the *quantum vacuum*, a so called *quantum ether, morphogenetic fields,* 'dark energy'.

And each of these only hints at a part of the true Aether.

NT: There's supposed to be this seething mass of Zero Point energy. And then people imagine that there's some sort of field that explains all that's funny.

I take this seriously. I suspect that there is – and this is what I'd like to come on to – a true boundary between the physical and what we're calling the Aetheric. And they actually are not dualistic. They are part and parcel of each other. They work with one another hand in glove. And if you restrict your perceptions to purely physical things then you hit a boundary which is called the Zero Point energy. That's the boundary where what's really going on is what we're calling the Aether – rightly calling the Aether.

And so you find this absurd idea of things coming into existence and vanishing within Heisenberg's principles.

If you think that through, it doesn't seem to work, to my mind anyway, that Heisenberg idea there. It seems to me they've turned the thing on its head. But be that as it may – that's rather technical – and what we come to is that kind of boundary, the probability boundary, the chaos boundary.....

EB: And what you're saying, Nick, is, all these boundaries represent the limitations of our own understanding.

TEST 3: EFFICIENT OPERATION?

So long as Western science remains locked into the mindset that the ultimate reality is a random, material-physical universe, it will remain dysfunctional and thus operate inefficiently. However, appreciating the coherence that awareness of the Aether brings could begin to rectify that very quickly.

Next, we'll look briefly at two of the essential – qualities we need to have in mind at all times when thinking about the Aether. Then we'll consider that most elusive something known as *consciousness*.

Wholeness

NT: Is there one governing principle to my conception of the Aether?

What that has proved to be essentially is wholeness. The wholistic aspects of what's around us lie, really, at the centre of all that we talk about as Aether.

Engineers deal with *whole*, functioning systems and know that it's the *relationships* between all the parts and the whole – as much as the parts themselves – that determine how well a system functions. It's also understood that behind every system there's a *design*, a purpose, which is the reason for its very existence as a system, complete in its wholeness.

NT: Our ordinary science deals very effectively and very well with all that has to do with breaking it down into little bits and you understand all the little bits and then you try to put the little bits together again.

And that is a very valuable approach but it's only half the story. And the other half of the story is, when you try to put it together again, what is the togetherness?

The great German poet Goethe once said that, you take a butterfly and you pin it to your board, and there you have all these beautiful butterflies – dead. And you've lost the butterflies. And in a sense that's what reductionism does. You lose that whole essence.

And so the Aether part of it...my conception of the Aether, or what's an essential part of my conception of the Aether, is just that wholeness.

The very word *particle* means 'a little part' which must be, by definition, part of a greater wholeness.

We're aware of *wholeness* when we see something as an entity in itself, rather than as a collection of parts – when we see a cat rather than an assembly of limbs, fur, ears, eyes etc, or when we see a car rather than a heap of components.

NT: Well, what it comes down to, I think, is that what we sense, those of us who are more open to the wholistic side, is just that there is a wholism and wholism isn't just a word. It's actually very precise.

       I mean take, say, the wholeness of your face or my face. Few people stop to wonder how it is you see a face as a whole. And it was in that book, *The Man Who Mistook His Wife For a Hat* – I don't know if you've read that one?....

DL: I know who you mean. It was Oliver Sacks.

NT: Oliver Sacks' book. There's an incredible case he cites of a patient who could not see faces. He could see a nose, or a scar, or anything unusual about the face, and he'd say, 'Oh, Hello Jim', or whoever. But if your face didn't have anything unusual like a scar or something like that, he couldn't see who you were.

       Now this ability to see , or experience wholeness, is something we take absolutely for granted every day of our lives. That's something which I think is actually Aetheric. I think that's something where we have a consciousness that is related to the wholeness in a way that no reductionist approach can ever hope to come near to.

Western science has so far tended to limit itself to the opposite perspective. It continues to be obsessed with analysing and measuring the component parts, and reducing everything down to ultimate 'building blocks' and 'fundamental' (or elementary) particles – as if these are somehow more 'real' than the whole thing to which they belong.

Yet we all know that simply reassembling the parts of what was once a whole living being doesn't bring back the missing aliveness. And the question always remains: What are the building blocks themselves made of – smaller building blocks?

Professor of Biology, **Brian Goodwin**, sees it like this.

BG:　　…It's like elementary particle physics. there's no end to particles, if you want to look at things from that point of view.

　　　　It's endless….the cataloguing can go on and on for ever.

So there are no ultimate building blocks to be found in this continuously shifting and transforming universe.

Paradoxically, the all-inclusive, *unifying theory* has long been the great aspiration of Western science, even as it has become increasingly specialized and fragmented into many mutually exclusive disciplines and theories.

But that quest is always self-sabotaged by the tendency to reduce and break wholeness down into parts.

Western science's best attempt so far has been its so called *Standard Model*. However, this does not as yet include *gravity*. And the eminent physicist **Richard Feynman's** comment was: *"So we are stuck with a theory, and we do not know whether it is right or wrong, but we do know that it is a little wrong, or at least incomplete."*

The young science of *Ecology* in the latter 20th century did reintroduce the ancient wisdom idea of the living Earth as the physical, organic body of a whole, conscious being. It taught that *Nature* is a self-sustaining, self-regulating, recycling process, all the parts of which are interdependent.

But this inspiring knowledge has been sabotaged by mainstream Western science, which artificially straps Ecology to *Economics* – in the sense of all ecological considerations having a price tag attached, as if this is the ultimate measure of their worth.

However, to a practical engineer, *Economics* is a false science, serving as the creed of a fundamentally flawed belief system. It masquerades as a science by using lots of graphs, diagrams, mathematics and pseudo-scientific 'laws'. Economics is, essentially, an attempt to rationalize *capitalism*.

That is, it tries to justify the accumulation of excessive resources into the hands of a few. This violates the de-centralising nature of the Aether. And such unwholesome growths obstruct the free flow of life, leading to imbalances and stagnation.

And it's all been built on false assumptions: first, that there is a scarcity on Earth of the basic necessities for all humankind to live a decent, healthy life. That's the *fear* generator.

The next false assumption is: that competitive, greed-motivated behaviour is a universal fact of human nature. Economists then build this into their calculations and predictions.

And when it's all entangled with a very complicated money system – cleverly manipulated – the result is a jungle, impenetrable to all but a select few.

Money itself can be understood as essentially *aethereal*, in that it's really just an idea – potential energy in token form, which can be transformed into action or material things and back again. This theme is developed later in the project.

That greater order in the cosmos which scientists continue to seek is an expression of *wholeness*. What we call morals and ethics arise from that wholeness. However, the implicit teaching of Economics is that in competing we can ignore any idea of moral or ethical responsibility – and thus wholeness.

Economics is a creed of greed, preached worldwide, a creed based on the fear which arises from ignorance of such essentials as the Aether, a creed which creates a poisoned atmosphere.

Meanwhile, the fate of *Ecology* serves as a warning to those doing any new scientific work which may go against the dogma of the established orthodoxy.

Next we consider one essential principle we need in order to understand *wholeness*, at all levels of the cosmos. And that is *polarity*.

Polarity

Polarity is essentially a simple idea. It's about the balance achieved between opposed forces within any system – which means that the poles, defining those forces, are always in a dynamic, complementary relationship. The North and South Poles of the Earth and the positive and negative poles of a battery are the most immediately obvious examples.

Primary polarities are the universal governing principles of our universe, such as *Gravity* and its long-denied polar opposite, *Levity*.

Oriental cultures have a similar polarity in *Yang and Yin*. And these give rise to *contraction and expansion, inward and outward* between *centre and periphery*.

Light and dark are also primary. Exploring their polarity leads to powerful insights regarding the whole phenomenon of *colour*. Too much light or dark in our lives is harmful. And the balance between them is certainly not a grey compromise – as we'll see later in this Report.

One polarity we can all identify with is that between the universal *masculine* and *feminine principles.*

A main feature of the *masculine* principle is thrusting and penetrating inwards from the periphery towards the centre, while the *feminine* principle is more about receiving, containing and extending from the centre outwards towards the periphery.

Here we need to distinguish clearly between these *universal* principles and the *specific* differences of male and female *gender*. The masculine and *feminine* are always to be found combined in each physical creature – both *male* and *female*.

A deeper exploration of *polarity* and the *Aether* can also bring powerful insights into such apparent mysteries as the origins of *gender* as well as *sex* and *death*. And it can lead to a practical, non-religious understanding of *good* and *evil*.

Edi Bilimoria again,

EB: The minute you emerge from a state of wholeness there is always polarity.

NT: Well, it depends how you want to approach it. I'm trying to build a bridge between our experience of this world and the way we would experience if we lived in the world of the Aether. And those two kinds of experiences are polar opposite.

Our experience of everyday life, ordinarily, is point centred, I suppose you'd say, geometrically. It says, I'm at a point of the universe and I'm looking out towards an infinity which is infinitely far away. But then, if you go into another realm, into another kind of space where the Aether exists, this space is like a sort of opposite of our ordinary space. It's not an aspect of our ordinary space. It is it's own space – it's quite separate.

But <u>there</u> you have to have a consciousness as it were turned inside out and it's looking <u>in</u> from the periphery always, infinitely inwards.

So there you get a polarity straight away.

When you get two real polarities interacting with one another, then something happens.

EB: You have a third factor that emerges always.

NT: Precisely

Three-ness, or *threefoldness*, is thus an essential aspect of all polarity. The vital *third factor* can be thought of as either that which mediates between the two poles at their interface or, the greater wholeness of which they are both parts.

It's the lack of polarity that exposes the *Black Hole* theory in physics as a simplistic 'boy mentality' idea embellished with some clever mathematics. It's basically a *materialistic misconception*, derived, however, from an intuitive sensing of a deep truth.

Black Holes have been presented as overwhelmingly *inward* processes, dominated by extreme gravity, with a *singularity* point of ultimate gravity.

This is masculine, 'particle' thinking.

Newton affirmed the principle of universal *polarity* in his description, mentioned earlier, of the universal *contracting* and *expanding* forces of the *Aether*.

In contrast to *polarity* is the <u>binary</u> way of thinking – that is, dividing everything into separate, mutually exclusive, *either-or, one-thing-or-the-other* opposites, such as *yes-<u>or</u>-no, on-<u>or</u>-off, black-<u>or</u>-white, friend-<u>or</u>-foe* and so on.

This is the basis of *digital* technology. And it's the product of minds reduced down to a point-centred view of the world, without any real notion of wholeness.

However, once we realize this, we then have the power of choice as to whether to view any situation from a specific point within it or from the wholeness of it.

From an engineering perspective however, the *binary* way of thinking crucially fails to acknowledge that <u>both</u> poles are always parts of a larger system, ie are always included within a greater wholeness. And this inclusiveness, which is lacking in the digital way, is fundamental to how Nature functions. It could be the basis of a whole new generation of *analogue technology* – analogous, that is, to Nature.

Also ignored in binary thinking is the influence our own presence has on any situation. And this is something with which Quantum physicists have long been grappling, as we'll see later.

Here the *observer* is the essential *third factor*.

All of which leads the practical engineer to the alarming conclusion of an impending global disaster. For the digital way is to keep adding on more bits.

And already today no human mind can comprehend the degree of complication in any major digital system. It's this inherent weakness that leaves us powerless and bound for major breakdowns and the collapse of whole superstructures now completely dependent on digital technology – in the same way that a bridge, building or machine with a built-in, fundamental design flaw, is doomed from the start.

This ultimate fragmentation of information – the great *digital delusion*, as some would call it – also serves as a major distraction. It prevents us from directly engaging with and experiencing Nature and the cosmos. We end up with elaborately detailed assemblies of bits – brilliant sandcastle simulations which are, however, unreliable and prone to disintegration... crashing.

Are there any alternative ways? The answer is: Yes, if given the same level of investment that's gone into digital technology. But again, that's a subject way beyond the scope of this Report.

Wisdom, some would say, is the balancing of the polaric forces in any situation, thereby achieving a feeling of wholeness. By contrast, we can see Western science becoming ever more unbalanced and set against religion – which itself then appears more welcoming and attractive, however distorted some of the hidden motives of those involved may be.

The *polarity* with which this whole project is particularly concerned is that between the *aethereal* and the *physical* realms – corrsponding to which are the two primary polar forces of the cosmos, *Levity* and *Gravity*.

And the crucial area of that polarity is the *threshold*, the boundary, the border, the interface between these two realms.

And, as we'll discover in this project, many of the apparent mysteries and anomalies of Nature begin to reveal an underlying coherence, once we apply the universal principle of polarity within wholeness.

Consciousness

NT: When we're thinking, we are exercising our Aetheric body.
        Basically, it's as simple as that. Thoughts are aetheric. That's
        why psychology has an awful job to pin them down, because it
        thinks they're something going on in the brain. And then they
        don't understand the wholistic action of the brain. Of course
        not. It's aetheric.

        A different consciousness is indeed required to comprehend
        the Aether. And that's just why generally we find it difficult in
        ordinary life and in science to comprehend the Aether –
        because we try to do so with our ordinary consciousness. And
        just to give a brief idea of what that different consciousness is
        like: you have to actually imagine it being turned inside out. If
        you can imagine yourself sort of being turned inside out, very
        thoroughly, not just superficially, but <u>totally</u> being turned inside
        out, so that in the end your awareness is sitting in the
        periphery and you're sort of looking infinitely inward – a sort of
        godlike consciousness really, and you're looking in from the
        periphery at all that's within you, rather than our ordinary
        consciousness where you're looking at all that's outside you.

        Our ordinary consciousness is a very comfortable one: I'm here
        and everything else is out there. This other consciousness is
        completely different: I'm here and I'm embracing everything.
        And we don't always want to embrace everything. There are
        things that we don't want to embrace at all. So it requires a
        certain personal development to be able to deal with such a
        consciousness.

ENGINEER'S ASSUMPTION – *Consciousness* is the
fundamental, primordial state of being of the cosmos, and is
<u>not</u> the result of physical-material processes, which are a
later development. Therefore, there is no polar opposite of

consciousness – only degrees of its development, which gives us a wide range of levels of consciousness, from sleeping to waking states.

There's our *individual* self consciousness. There's the *group* or *collective* consciousness we share with others in some common idea or ideal. And then there's a sense of *universal* consciousness we may experience when in a transcendental state of being.

How easily our consciousness may be influenced by others can be seen in the way a hypnotist or a conjurer works or in the power of advertising and propaganda, as well as in the arts – and especially if we are not conscious that there is an *aethereal* level of our being at which this is happening.

And since consciousness defies any simple definition of what it is, we build up an impression by approaching it from various angles.

Eugene Wigner, a contemporary leading physicist, has said – contrary to the false assumption of most western scientists – that:

> *"The very study of the external world led to the conclusion that the content of the consciousness is the ultimate reality."*

And we know that while all the matter constituting our physical bodies is continuously disintegrating and being replaced, our individual sense of identity, our consciousness, continues.

KEY QUESTION – How can it be established that consciousness is the ground state of the cosmos?

OVERVIEW
Before the 1930s, in Western science, the *consciousness* of

the experimenter was not thought of as a significant factor in experiments and was therefore not an issue. But as *Quantum Physics* began to grapple with the extremely small, subtle and sensitive sub-atomic realm, it became a <u>central</u> issue. And in the early 1930s it was accepted that the observer, as a conscious being, cannot avoid affecting whatever is being observed.

We've already heard **Professor Roger Penrose** say that there's something vital missing in Physics, which is crucial to the phenomenon of consciousness.

This implies that to find what's missing we need to go <u>beyond</u> present day *Quantum Physics*.

(Here his words, again from a recent broadcast, are spoken by an actor.)

RP: As a scientific problem the 'consciousness problem' is more profound because we have no clue . . .

Consciousness is a gift – we can look at it that way perhaps. Consciousness is a gift in the sense that we wouldn't be here without it. And it's given to us all. I mean, we came into the world and we seem to possess the thing of consciousness. Whereas the ability to reflect on one's own consciousness is something you've done yourself. You've thought about this. You've thought this through, in a sense. I mean if you were a deity trying to design the universe, what ingredients would you have to put into this design for a universe in order that these beings in it actually have consciousness? We haven't the remotest idea.

We don't know what the main physical laws are. It's not a normal view for a physicist that there should be these profound unknowns. I mean, a lot of people will try to say, 'Well, we don't completely understand all the laws but we pretty well know what's going on. There are certain things we don't understand about particle physics or about the universe as a whole...'

But they don't tend to say, 'There is something profoundly missing in the physical laws at a level of relevance to how we ourselves operate.' Whereas I think there is.

My view is that at a certain level things are going to change. The laws of quantum mechanics are not completely accurate at all levels and I have reasons to believe that the physics that we now miss here, which is quite fundamental, is also <u>the same physics which is made use of by the phenomenon of consciousness</u>. I don't want to say it's the same as consciousness. But whatever consciousness is, it depends upon that missing part of physics.

Once again, it has to be remembered that Physics limits itself to the physical-material realm only. It is thus not competent to consider the nature of the non-physical Aether, which is the key to accessing the more subtle realms of reality – including consciousness.

DL: Scientists have now realised that they can't simply take an exclusively third person perspective on things, ie. just looking from the outside in, when our whole understanding arises from consciousness, which is from the inside out.

NT: It's primary. That's right. We begin there. We don't begin from matter, actually, in maths. We begin from our human experience, don't we?

DL: Well, we have to. Really, it's stating the obvious, but it needs to be stated. It's like the fish that couldn't see the sea and actually was in the sea all the time – you weren't allowed to talk about consciousness, even though you had to be conscious in order not to be allowed to talk about it.

Here is what another leading contemporary physicist, **John Wheeler**, has said: *"Participator, is the incontrovertible new concept."*

All this has proved very challenging for people steeped in the belief that science is 'objective', with the experimenter merely a neutral observer, not affecting what's going on.

Here's Professor of Biology, **Brian Goodwin**:

BG: …with ecosystems, with organisms, we're finally recognising that we have to be participants..... So what we have is the possibilty of a science of qualities. It's the way Goethe did his science, and many other people.

Meanwhile, Western science is still trying to reduce *consciousness* and *psychology* – given that *psyche* means *soul* – down to what we might more accurately call *'Brainism'*. That is, the misconception that physical processes in the brain are the original cause of all that we consciously experience.

Measurable physical processes may well be found occurring simultaneously with conscious experiencing, but they are not in any way the same thing. They are the outer, gross expressions of more subtle inner events – just as a the tail doesn't wag the dog into a state of excitement, a high body temperature is not the cause but the symptom of a fevered condition and a fluttering flag doesn't cause the wind to blow.

And stimulating inner experiences artificially by an electric current only works if the capacity for those experiences is already there within.

From a practical engineering perspective, the *brain* is bodily matter in the skull, ingeniously <u>utilised</u> as an instrument for registering, ordering and processing information.

It doesn't itself think – any more than some part of a car *desires* to go for a drive – although systems can be pre-programmed to appear to be self-motivated.

And since human heart transplant operations have become common practice, a number of doctors and professors have been studying how *recipients* have taken on personal traits and memories of the *donor*. Consequently the emerging science of the 'brain in the heart' has been radically challenging the old materialistic assumptions – regarding both heart as only a mechanical pump and brain as the exclusive centre of thinking and emotion.

The nerve centre in the heart has been found to respond to events first and then send impulses to the brain, which implies a kind of intuitive reacting. According to one of the doctors, the heart seems to be connecting to what he calls a 'field of information'.

Viewed in the context of the all-permeating Aether or Akasha – with every living entity being the physical embodiment of its aetheric form – the strange experience of someone else's presence in your own personality begins to make some sense. Also the electromagnetic field around the heart has been found to be five thousand times more powerful than that of the brain.

Materialism, as exemplified by Western science, is the result of consciousness becoming too deeply embedded in matter, and losing touch with the more subtle levels of being.

NT: Suppose you have a whole lot of robots, and they say, 'There are no such things as human beings; that's a superstition.' And one of them says, 'Look at that car driving down there. How is it steered and controlled?' So the robot goes and has a look at it and he can't see human beings, you see. And he says, 'Oh, it's very simple. When the car wants to go to the left, that wheel there turns and that makes it go to the left. And when it wants to slow down, that thing on the floor there, that pedal-kind-of-lever thing.... I've noticed that, I've observed, (in the million dollar research project from the Robot University).... that goes down towards the floor and the car slows down!

And this is what our reductionist explanations are like. We're finding lots of steering wheels turning and brake pedals being pushed. And we're not asking, Why? Because if we actually asked we'd know that there's something involved with that steering wheel.

Perhaps it's timely that recently biologist and Nobel Laureate, **Sir Paul Nurse**, has claimed that cells exhibit *consciousness* and *purpose* – both of which only a few years ago were taboo words in Western science.

On BBC Radio 4's Start the Week, he said the following: (His words are spoken by an actor)

PN: Well, you take a brick from a cathedral and it's just a brick. You take a cell from your body and we can grow it, and it will reproduce, and it acts as a living thing. It has purpose.

What I mean by purpose is that .... it's a word that has been coined by the great biologist Jacques Monot, '*telionomic*' (is endowed with purpose). And this is what living things have.

It's not simple pure chemistry, though there's lots of chemistry going on in there. It's organised chemistry that gives a purpose to that cell. It can grow. It can organise itself in space. It can organise itself in time: it persists and changes in time. It can reproduce. It can respond to the environment in specific ways.

That's what I mean by purpose – a sort of higher order response beyond the chemistry. And that higher order response is life.

> A real Holy Grail for biologists is to understand what biological organisation is all about. What distinguishes this test tube full of chemical reactions from a living cell? So what is the nature of biological organisation?
>
> We're taught at school never to talk in those terms – that cells could <u>know</u> what they are. We have to put ourselves inside the cell and imagine knowing what it's doing and how it's organised. Just knowing how a cell organises itself in space is an extraordinary achievement that we simply don't understand.

What Paul Nurse is describing we can interpret as the normal functioning of the *Life Aether*, which works at all levels of living Nature – from populations, species and individual organisms down to cells and DNA.

It's the *'higher order'* he refers to, beyond mere physical survival and information processing – it's more about each living entity fulfilling its seed potential, its destiny.

An engineer assumes that every working system – a telephone network, an army, a computer – whatever it does, is the realisation of a *conscious intention*, a *purpose*. This is essentially its *meaning* – what it's meant to do.

And now biologists, as we've heard, are beginning to recognise the signs of a universal conscious *intent* motivating the whole living world – which does have profound implications for all scientific thinking from here on.

Gaining some appreciation of the *aethereal* level of being opens up the possibility of better understanding the nature of *feelings* and emotion, and then of *purpose* or *will*.

THE ENGINEER'S 3 TESTS

– regarding Western science and Consciousness

TEST 1: SOUND PRINCIPLES?

The *Brainism* fallacy, promoted by Western science, is the result of its delusion, or pretence, that the *physical* is the ultimate reality. As such, it's a very <u>un</u>sound foundation on which to base any truly scientific investigation into consciousness. That is because it ignores the worldwide acknowledgement of non-physical states of being.

DL: The way it's formulated, the so-called 'hard problem', How does the brain give rise to consciousness? That's the wrong question.

NT: Exactly

DL: It's the wrong question. So no wonder it's a hard problem. It's an <u>impossible</u> problem to resolve within that particular framework.

NT: Well it was.... in *New Scientist*, I think it was , a year or two ago, they came up with some materialistic explanations for out-of-body experiences: there's some little loop somewhere in the brain and this is what causes them. And of course these people don't seem to practise the most rudimentary logic and thinking. Because, if you take a lot of the descriptions where people have had an out-of-the-body experience – and I know these people and you know them – and they can come back and present you with quite definite data which could not have been given by a loop in the brain. It had to have been acquired by being there. Like George Ritchie who travelled into another town and could come back and tell you the name of the streets and the shops there.

Well you don't get that from a loop in the brain.

TEST 2: ELEGANT DESIGN?

When the underlying assumptions of scientists regarding consciousness have little or nothing to do with the <u>qualities</u> of consciousness we actually experience, *elegance of design* is out of the question.

Electrical, mechanical or mathematical models of consciousness, or animals used in experiments, may produce some impressive statistics.

But it's simply not valid to try to translate *subjective, aethereal* experience into *objective physical* data.

NT: If you listen to a sound, if you listen to violin playing or something.... we can describe the pressure waves, of course, that go through the air. And we can do elegant experiments, we can cut them out and let them in again...there are pressure waves going into this microphone right now. But that's not what we hear. We don't hear pressure waves, we hear sound, tone.

And if we go into the essence of the <u>experience</u> of tone – not the theory of physics about sound and pressure waves.... Pressure waves exist. Sure. But I'm not interested in them. I'm interested in what I experience – the timbre, the quality of a violin, the quality of a piano. That's on the Aetheric level. That's something that nobody knows, what these perceptions are.

Nobody in the world, no philosopher knows where 'yellowness', the sound of a violin, where it comes from.

A physicist would describe all these waves pouring into us – 'and then they go in the eye and the ear and pour into the brain and all sorts of fantastic things happen in the brain. I've no quibble with any of that. But I would like them to tell me how they build a bridge between all that fascinating stuff and <u>what I actually experience</u>.

Similarly, the intangible, aethereal qualities we experience in a musical performance cannot be reduced down to symbols on paper or on a screen.

EB: For example I can think of the great Nobel Laureate, Schroedinger, who said that science in principle can tell us why an old tune can move us to tears in terms of describing the mechanics of a salty gland in the eyes secreting a fluid and the brain neurochemistry. 'But <u>why</u> an old tune, a beautiful song should move us to tears, science is ghastly silent' – I'm quoting Schroedinger – 'and it does not even pretend to address these issues.'

TEST 3: EFFICIENT OPERATION?

Western science's models and theories simply can't cope with the range, complexity and fluidity of the human psyche. So they will inevitably be inadequate and therefore inefficient in aiding understanding. For example, in the case of a divided consciousness in a near-death experience.

Back with **David Lorimer**.

DL: I've always been fascinated – I don't know if you know this case? – by the Geddes case, Sir Auckland Geddes case... when he was dying. He suddenly felt very ill. In fact he realised he was dying. And then he describes how his, 'A consciousness' ....(he was a medical doctor)..... separated from his 'B consciousness'. The 'B consciousness' stayed with the body and the 'A consciousness' could <u>see</u> the body. And then he started realising that the 'A consciousness' could see anywhere it directed its attention.

So he was able to direct his attention to the hospital where somebody had just called to get the doctor out and so he heard the doctor's – or rather, *saw* – the doctor's thought, which was then translated into a hearing.

And he said he found himself free in a time dimension of space where 'here' was equivalent to 'now' And so, in some sense, either you could say that the time dimension had collapsed and it didn't take him any time to go from *a* to *b*, or you could say that the space dimension had collapsed because he was everywhere at once.

And then he was just beginning to understand what was happening to him – it was quite subtly expressed – when the doctor arrived, gave him an injection, and he was pulled back into the body. And he said "all that was left was a glimmer of consciousness suffused with pain."

One essential stage in developing Aether awareness is to make the necessary mental 'flip', or inversion.

That is, to turn our consciousness inside out from its normal worldview.

NT: One of the interesting aspects of consciousness, of course, is that if you have a really thoroughgoing out-of-body experience, there's this experience of turning inside out. A lot of the experiences that are described aren't that thorough, that far. They go so far – there's a black tunnel, or whatever it is, a being of light... Very often the consciousness doesn't go far enough.

But when I've given talks on, for instance, my work, people will very often come up and say, 'Yes, I have had that complete turning inside out of consciousness.' Where it's as though you're looking in from the cosmic periphery, rather than, as we are now, sitting at a point in space looking outwards – you're sort of looking inwards.

What is very interesting about that is, there's another kind of space one can describe, within which such a consciousness can exist. And the whole space is like the negative of our space. And when you have experience in such a space, with this other kind of consciousness, then you have an awareness of the wholism of the world in a way you never do in pure theory.

And that's what I'm interested in as the Aetheric. It's a step towards the spiritual. It isn't in fact the spiritual but it is if you like a step in that direction.

DL: It's a bridge. Or a level, if you like.

And to put the subject of consciousness in its bigger cosmic context, we can usefully consider the whole notion of *cosmic* and *human* evolution as the **evolution of consciousness** itself:

NT: Cosmic evolution <u>is</u> a process of evolving consciousness. And we look at all these wonderful forms around us, the living forms, the animal forms – they're all, in their own way manifestations of a particular level of consciousness.

And to make that a little bit more precise, the lower down the level you go.... one might ask, well, in what sense lower? Lower in the sense of <u>specific sharpness</u>. But in another sense much broader. The so-called lower levels of life actually have a very much broader kind of consciousness, a consciousness that reaches much further out into the cosmos than ours does.

You and I, if we're feeling good – it's a good day, we're sharp, we're awake, everything's going for us – then we're very particularly <u>here and now</u>. I've no consciousness of what's going on in the village and in our High Street, much less what's going on on Mars. I have a consciousness of this room, of you, of our being here together, but no consciousness outside that. At the most, if an aircraft flies over, my consciousness goes out on the wings of sound maybe, and meets that aircraft. But then I'm back here again. Whereas much lower organisms seem to have a consciousness that exists very much more widely.

Perhaps some of the clearest examples of that are, for instance, the flights of birds, migrations of birds. And there's an astonishing consciousness of the earth as a whole, as one thinks of birds migrating thousands, perhaps tens of thousands of miles.

And if one thinks about it, and doesn't turn off one's thinking, one becomes aware that there's some relationship to wholeness there that's astonishing – a consciousness that's extending much wider than our consciousness does.

Animals are capable of doing things that we seem quite incapable of and yet we're supposed to be much more highly evolved than they are. So one says, evolved in what sense?

So, I would say there's a polarity there in consciousness. There's this broad, dim kind of consciousness that reaches right out but is much less sharp. Then there's the very sharp consciousness that we have, that's confined to one location. And I think evolution is moving, has moved, from one to the other.

The next phase of evolution is going to be bringing those two together. As we move further into the future I think human evolution will be an extension of the sharpness, the accuracy, the awakeness we've now acquired. That will be extended into that broadness. One can imagine in the far future a consciousness that extends over the whole universe but is also sharp.

We move on in the next section to the closely related topic

of **Light** and **Darkness**. This continues to be a subject of much misconception and misguided teaching, and includes what have now become blocks of unquestioned *dogma*. The dogma is based both on a misconception of Newton's, and on some of the highly contrived imaginary situations of the young Einstein.

And therein lie the reasons for the difficulty just about everyone has when first trying to grasp Einstein's **Theory of Relativity.**

We'll see how the idea of *polarity-within-wholeness* helps overcome these inbuilt problems.

Light and Darkness

NT: We never see light. We only see things <u>with</u> light.

ENGINEER'S ASSUMPTION – The one word, *light*, has several meanings, about which we need to be clear. For all is not as it seems regarding *light* and its polar opposite, *darkness*.

NT: Light is invisible. Light Aether is invisible. It characterises in a wonderful way the whole issue of Aether. The Aether is something not sense perceptible but it enables us to have sense percepts.

It's the selfless invisible agent always there. You see it doesn't intrude upon you. It doesn't make itself felt; it makes the objects around you felt instead.

KEY QUESTION – How can we scientifically reach a fuller understanding and appreciation of this multi-levelled phenomenon we call *light* and its relationship to what we call *dark* or *darkness*?

OVERVIEW

Modern Quantum Physics has, in a back-to-front way, arrived at an ancient way of understanding light. The ancient way says that at an early, pre-physical stage of the cosmos, there emanated from the oneness a universal, primeval and timeless *Radiant Light*, also long known in the West as the *Aether*. It's <u>invisible</u> to our *physical eyes* and is thus perceived as *darkness*.

Arthur Zajonc, Professor of Physics at Amherst College, Massachusetts, and author of the much acclaimed book, *Catching The Light*, describes in it a very simple demonstration of the principle:

AZ: As part of what I call Project Eureka, a friend and I have
        designed and constructed a science exhibit in which one views
        a region of space filled with light. It is a simple but startling
        demonstration that uses only a carefully fabricated box and a
        powerful projector whose light shines directly into it. We have
        taken special care to ensure that light does not illuminate any
        interior objects or surfaces in the box. Within the box there is
        only pure light and lots of it. The question is, What does one
        see? How does light look when left entirely to itself?

        Approaching the exhibit, I turn on the projector, whose bulb
        and lenses can be seen through a plexiglas panel. The
        projector sends a brilliant light, through optical elements, into
        the box beside it. Moving over to a viewport, I look into the
        box and at the light within. What do I see? Absolute darkness. I
        see nothing but the blackness of empty space.

        On the outside of the box is a handle connected to a wand
        that can move into and out of the box's interior. Pulling the
        handle, the wand flashes through the dark space before me
        and I see the wand brilliantly lit on one side. The space is
        clearly not empty but filled with light. Yet, without an object
        on which the light can fall, one sees only darkness. Light is
        always invisible. We see only things, only objects. Not light.

        The exhibit reminds me of a conversation I had over dinner
        with the Apollo astronaut, Rusty Schweikhart. I asked him
        about his space walk, specifically about what he saw when
        looking out into the sunlit emptiness of outer space. He replied
        that although it was difficult to keep the brightly lit spacecraft
        and other hardware out of view, if you could do so, then you
        saw only the dark depths of deep space studded with the light
        of countless stars. The Sun's light, although present
        everywhere, fell on nothing, and so nothing was seen, only
        darkness.

Regarding light and Aether, Professor Zajonc has also said: *"The figure of sound is borne by the air. What bears the fleeting figure we call light? One thing has become certain, whatever it is, it is not material."*

That non-material 'something' has been the subject of much speculation. And the current idea in physics of a universally present, so-called 'dark energy' – which implies that it's invisible – indicates a rather desperate groping for something very much like the non-material *Aether*.

We can now clearly distinguish two kinds of light:
First, there's the primary, invisible, pure, aethereal, cosmic light.

And then there's the secondary kind of light, *physical light* – visible because it's *Light Aether* interacting with matter – whether gas, liquid or solid. And this gives us the familiar colour range of the electro-magnetic spectrum.

Light, as the *colour spectrum*, visible to our physical eyes, was the subject of much disagreement back in Newton's time. And his theory is still the one favoured by the science orthodoxy.

But a very different *theory of light*, proposed by the German poet, playwright and scientist **Goethe**, makes far more practical sense from an engineer's perspective.

NT: Goethe studied actual colour and that's why very few scientists take Goethe seriously, or at least until recently – they've started to again more now. But Goethe was never taken all that seriously because he studied colour rather than a theory about colour. And so he studied the red end of the spectrum and the blue end of the spectrum and these phenomena and what happens when light and darkness come into relationship with one another.

His theory was that you have darkness and light and when the two interact with one another in a real way you get polarity. You take a prism, and what a prism does according to Goethe is to make dark and light interact with one another and then you get the glorious colours that you get in a prism.

AZ: Let me give you a simple example drawn from Goethe's own work in colour theory: We stand in an open field, we look out into the blue of the sky and we can ask the question which every child asks: Why is the sky blue?

And the answer which conventional physics will give you will be in terms of Rayleigh scattering. Or if it's a little more elaborate, in terms of what's called *mie* scattering. And there'll be the polarisability of small aerosols under the impress of electromagnetic fields. The differential cross section goes, like, the fourth power of the frequency, which means that high frequencies are scattered first. High frequencies correspond to blue and therefore the sky is blue. *(Audience laughter)*

And it's true. It's not a lie. But it's a <u>kind</u> of account. Can you feel the kind of account that it is?

It is in terms of a model. It is terms of the sign and word that Goethe was talking about. It's very powerful. It's very attractive. At least to me. But it's also a danger. A danger where we explain everything, including ourselves, our illnesses, our sufferings, all those perennial questions. We can't really account for them in terms of those signs and words.

And there's another way of seeing. And this way of seeing actually requires a certain transformation of the person in order to achieve. But nonetheless you can get a glimmer of it by standing in that same field and as opposed to seeing small aerosols you see the air itself has a quality to it. And that quality is, you could say, ambiguous. <u>It can act either, you</u>

<u>might say, as an agency of light or as an agency of darkness,</u> depending on the circumstance.

Imagine the sun over to the side filling the air above us with its glory, with its light...

And then we look through that medium of the atmosphere. We look through it into the depths of space. We know that if that air was absent, like it is on the Moon, we would see a black star-strewn heaven. Air carrying, you could say, the <u>luminosity</u> of the sunlight – we look through it and instead of looking through it into blackness we have the experience of blue. No location to that blue, just blueness throughout.

In other words there is a relationship between the darkness of space, the light of the sun and this medium of the air. And as long as that perceived relationship is present you actually have the conditions, you could say the organic conditions, <u>in which blue will arise</u>. And wherever you stand and wherever those conditions arise you see the congruence, the coherence in Nature which produces, you could say, or allows to arise, the experience of blue.

Another thing which is present, and which to me is very important, is that experience of blue is a <u>felt</u> experience.

When you laughed that sort of giddy little laugh about the fourth power of the differential cross section with the fourth power of the frequency, there's this sense of wonder and also estrangement. Right? You don't <u>feel</u> that differential cross section. It takes some work to get to <u>feel</u> differential cross sections. *(laughter)* But as you stand between darkness and light in this great medium of the atmosphere there's something which you have as you triangulate and you put yourself into that place of experience. And then the blue is not only an abstract production but actually a lived experience.

We can envisage Professor Zajonc standing in his field, right at the *threshold* of the *physical* and the *aethereal*. From there he is able to appreciate the truth and beauty of <u>both</u> views – in that complete, wholistic picture he sketches.

We'll briefly refer now to three of Western science's attempts to understand the nature of *light*, each of which seems fundamentally flawed on closer inspection.

And we'll remember that this kind of science treats all light as if it's <u>physical</u> – when it clearly isn't.

NT: First, Newton's Theory of Coloured Light.

Newton passed a beam of light through a prism and obtained a spectrum as a result and made the assumption that light then <u>contains</u> those colours, and that the prism, as it were, analyses or splits the light up.

But this approach lacks the real balance, the sense of polarity, which after all Newton did apply in some other areas of his work. And the result is a limited, and inadequate, account. For instance, Goethe pointed out that if you look through a prism, simply at a white wall or something, you don't get any colours at all. You only get colours as soon as there's an edge. And then one becomes aware of this role of polarity.

Professor Arthur Zajonc recalls in his book a re-run of a historic mid-20th century validation of Goethe's theory of light over Newton's – by none other than the inventor of the Polaroid camera:

AZ: In November of 1957, **Edwin Land**, the inventor of instant photography, lectured on colour, with demonstrations, to the National Academy of Sciences and to the Rockefeller Institute for Medical Research. His presentations, widely reported in the press, had startled the scientific community. In them, Land challenged the very foundations of contemporary colour theory. Six months later, Land lectured to the Royal Photographic Society in London. Land's demonstrations were truly astonishing. Nothing I had learned at the university could explain what I was seeing.

The standard basis for understanding colour had been laid down by Newton. With the subsequent advent of the Wave Theory of light the connection between colour and wavelength then became commonplace. Together these formed the orthodox framework for the understanding of colour. Land's experiments seemed to challenge the scientific notions of colour with a greater force than any previous experiments.

Newton had shown that if one extracted, say, yellow light from the spectrum produced by a prism and mixed it with orange light similarly produced, then a colour intermediate between the two, a yellow-orange, appeared. Its particular hue depended upon which colour dominated the mixture – orange or yellow.

Land performed the same experiment, but with a single important modification: he projected yellow and orange light beams through black and white photographic transparencies. The transparencies depicted an identical still life scene, but photographed through different coloured filters. With only the yellow image projected, one saw a purely monochrome yellow still life on the screen. None of the original colours of the scene were present. Only shades of yellow. The same was true when the second image alone was projected through the orange filter. The still life was entirely in shades of orange.

With Newton in mind, what would you expect to see if <u>both</u> images were projected on top of one another? Hues somewhere between yellow and orange, as before – that is what I expected. And most of the members of the National

Academy of Sciences expected the same. However, you do not see yellow-oranges. Far from it. Re-enacting Land's demonstrations I saw what happened to be a full range of colours, including reds, blues and greens. But these were colours I knew simply could not be there.

My eyes told one story. My training as a physicist told another. What was going on?

One answer, from this engineer's perspective, would be that Newton's theory of light is seriously flawed. Goethe's more wholistic and *polarity*-based theory, however, <u>can</u> help explain the apparent mystery.

And it's perhaps worth noting again that Edwin Land's invention is called the *polaroid* camera.

NT: The second flawed idea of Western science regarding light is the supposition that light has a constant velocity or speed.

Now according to ordinary physics, light travels through space with a definite velocity. This goes back some hundreds of years to the work of Romer who observed the moons of Jupiter appearing apparently late. And he explained that with the idea that light has a velocity. However, when one looks more closely at light and the way it behaves, it should be observed that all our physical measurements are measurements of what happens in the apparatus <u>at the moment of absorbtion of light</u>.

One cannot do any experiments on light without absorbing it into physical substance. And the assumption is then made that what happens at that moment of interaction between the light and the apparatus is happening all the way out.

For instance, it's imagined that because, at the last minute, as the light is absorbed into the apparatus, a wavelike nature can be discerned and a velocity apparently determined, the

assumption is that it's a wave with a velocity all through the whole universe. That is only an assumption.

And with our Aether concept we come to realise that what is thought of as the velocity of light is nothing of the sort. It's actually a constant of a different kind.

Pure light itself, being Aether, is universally present and therefore does not 'travel', and consequently does not have a velocity as such. The exception would be in the very limited case of the front of a beam or cone of *physical* light instantly filling a space. And its speed would depend on the density of the medium in that space.

This process can be loosely compared with the way air instantly fills a vacuum and is thereafter simply present in that space.

So, given that there is no universally constant *velocity of light*, questions inevitably arise concerning Einstein's famous $E = mc^2$. For we're left with c^2 as a meaningless symbol, representing the non-existent *velocity of light* multiplied by itself, and serving only as the required *constant* in the equation.

The c^2 is inaccurate in that what it represents is <u>not</u> a universal constant, however precise the measurements involved.

EB: **You can have something that's very precise that's totally fallacious. And people confuse quantitative precision with qualitative accuracy. You can have the graph to twenty-one decimal points but if your assumptions are wrong... and this is the whole point about a lot of science – far too much emphasis is put on logic and far too little emphasis is put on the underlying assumptions.**

You can build an Eiffel Tower of logic on very shaky sands. And the logic and the superstructure can be impregnable but it will topple over if your fundamental assumptions are shaky.

However, and for whatever reasons, once adopted by the Western science establishment, $E = mc^2$ soon became a central dogma of twentieth century physics. But to an open-minded engineer it looks like a perfect example of the *Emperor's New Clothes*. Alternatively, if the constant in the equation were, instead, the ever-present, all-pervading Aether, it would all be logically and scientifically consistent.

Nick Thomas has re-presented the *c* part of the equation, in mathematical terms, as a *scaling constant* representing the relationship between the realms or spaces of the aethereal and the physical.

Given the worlwide iconic status that Einstein's equation has acquired some further explanation is required. However, such an explanation would not be appropriate to this Report but can be found elsewhere, in the project.

EB: Modern science has done Einstein a great disservice, for a start, in turning 'the speed of light is constant' almost into a religious cult. This is nonsense. The speed of light is not constant. There is a lot of evidence, experimental evidence, to show it is not constant. It was made constant in order to make the results of Michelson-Morley fit Relativity.

And among the many serious implications arising from this fallacy are questions about the currently supposed size and age of the universe.

NT: As far as the size of the universe is concerned, here I need to touch upon the completely different concept of light that I'm working with: light doesn't travel.

It is a misconception of physics that light travels. It doesn't travel at all. And so we judge the size of the universe on the assumption that light travels at a certain velocity. If that assumption is wrong, as I believe it is – and I know that's total heresy but I've written a book where I justify it – if that heresy is correct, if light does not travel, then it means the judgements we're making about the size of the universe must be wrong because they're based upon that assumption.

What the size of the universe actually is, of course, remains a question. It could be very small. It could be much smaller than we think. Because it's quite possible that the light is coming into us... as the light, in its aetheric form, interacts with our apparatus, with our eyes, momentarily, in that <u>moment of interaction</u> – it's only very very short – then a wave arises and then we make all our calculations based on that wave. And we think it's come all the way as a wave. But actually it's a wave only at the very last minute. But we extrapolate back out. But it could have become a wave...it could have originated in something that's not very far away.

So, for me, the size of the universe is a totally open question. But I don't swallow the current figures in physics and astrophysics because, from a common sense point of view they're ludicrous.

I mean, stepping back a minute – you talk about the density of a neutron star, or the density of a Black Hole, you talk about the impossible processes that are supposed to take place in them – time having a different scale from what we know, an 'infinite singularity' that nobody's ever been able to explain...

And in fact, there was an article not so long ago. in a scientific magazine, where actually the astronomers and cosmologists have come clean and said that the whole theory of Black Holes is creaking at the seams. (It always has but they've only just admitted it) And why? I think the reason is because we've made these assumptions based upon the velocity of light being just that. We think light travels. If it doesn't then the whole thing is up for re-interpretation.

Of course for the age of the universe – how this affects our thinking about the age of the universe is equally profound because we judge the age based on the velocity of light again. We think it's travelled from such a huge distance, therefore it's been travelling for a huge amount of time. And of course that is also then an assumption which has to be questioned.

The rhythmic pulsating of the Aether behind the physical is a clue to understanding how Western science came to the idea of light travelling in *waves* – as opposed to the idea of light being composed of *particles*.

NT: The third flawed idea of Western science regarding light is the wave or particle paradox.

Quantum Physics regards the smallest amount of light that you can have as something called a *photon*. And a photon is imagined, in the first instance, to be something like some sort of little particle. Then experiments show that light also has a wave-like quality, apparently.

And so it becomes a little bit difficult to think about this photon in any clear way. Sometimes experiments give results as if light consisted of particles and other times experiments give results as if light was a wave – like a wave on water, with interference effects and those kinds of things. So, the question which has dogged science for the best part of a century or more now is this question: Is the photon a wave or a particle?

Now, in Quantum Mechanics such questions have no answer. Quantum Mechanics does not try to give any kind of factual answer of that nature. It's simply says that there are certain probabilities.

You don't need an in-depth knowledge of Physics to recognise this kind of practice – that is, experts using jargon to cover up their own failings.

NT: And so there they were wrestling with these things and a man called Schroedinger came up with something known as his wave equation. And he thought that matter was made of waves. It seemed to be quite a good idea at the time because there's always been this problem: Is it made of waves? Is it made of particles? Maybe it's one, maybe it's the other.... which has gone on since Newton..... Sometimes one, sometimes the other. We think. (I've got other ideas, but ...)

Anyway, Schroedinger thought that, Yes, electrons for instance, can act as waves. And he very brilliantly developed wave-mechanics and thought these waves were real waves of something. And then gradually, as the experiments got cleverer and cleverer and weirder and weirder, the idea that they're waves of anything disappeared. They couldn't be waves of anything for various technical reasons. So what were they waves of?

They were giving exquisite predictions of the outcomes of the experiments. And so in the end a man called Max Born re-interpreted those waves and said they are underlying the sort of statistical basis of the system. Those waves – you have to do a certain clever calculation of the waves and then you can calculate the probability of the particle that will pop up here.... or somewhere.

But to a practical engineer this is no more than an attempt to conceal an embarrassing gap in the theory with some abstract mathematics.

Now with the work I've been doing, I've come to the conclusion that we're really dealing with something Aetheric here. Waves but on completely another level. They are waves. They' re genuine waves. Not physical waves. So of course they can't be found physically.

The N C Thomas version says that pure, invisible light itself is aethereal and consists of neither particles nor waves. This version of photons agrees with the ancient idea of a universal polarity between the whole of cosmic space and any particular point.

NT: I think light is Aetheric in nature, by which I mean that light always bears a wholistic relationship to all its surroundings, rather than consisting of little rays or particles shooting out from a source, and is capable of relating at any moment any one specific location in the cosmos to any other specific location.

If you imagine a star, supposedly billions of miles away, emitting a lot of photons: it always amazes me that we can see that star. Isn't it rather lucky that enough photons happen, after coming through billions of miles, happen to exist in that minute solid angle in which the Earth exists as seen by that star?

I would have thought most of them would miss us and we'd get a flash of a photon from the star once every hundred years. Not at all. We see the thing the whole time continuously. And when you reflect on that you realise that there is some wholistic relationship between the star and us, mediated by its photons. The photons aren't particles. They can't be. We'd never see the distant stars.

Anyway, I could go on and on for ever, but perhaps that's enough for the moment.

THE ENGINEER'S 3 TESTS

– regarding Western science and its approach to Light and Dark

TEST 1: SOUND PRINCIPLES?

From what we've just been hearing, Western science is seriously lacking in sound principles regarding the essential nature of light and darkness.

NT: People try to identify colour with a wavelength of light or something. Well that's, of course, a confusion of categories. I've never quite understood how anybody can think that. It's just a simple confusion. What I experience as a colour is entirely different from what I might describe with maths as a wavelength. These two are different: one is a number, the other is the experience of a colour – a primary and a secondary quality. You can't just confuse them like that. It's nonsense.

TEST 2: ELEGANT DESIGN?

What we find in Western science are inconsistent and therefore inelegant theories concerning light. For ignoring observable evidence is always a sign of bad scientific practice, and for an engineer this would amount to professional irresponsibility.

TEST 3: EFFICIENT OPERATION?

When there are still so many unresolved paradoxes after so many years, Western science's approach evidently doesn't amount to an efficient operation.

Yet simply taking on board how light is both an aspect of the invisible Aether and how it also appears as colour, when combined with matter, could re-inspire and re-invigorate the whole of Western science.

With the overview we've gained here, many poetic and mystical sounding descriptions, ancient and modern, spiritual and otherwise, can be understood in a more direct and practical way – as expressions of humanity finding its place in the polarity of the cosmos.

For example, in the many references to the light and dark aspects of our world or to transcendental experiences.

We already have the notion clearly expressed in the idea of 'enlightenment'. We start out 'in the dark' regarding some particular aspect of the world in our consciousness . Then instantaneously, it seems, faster than any other event we can imagine, 'the light dawns on us', and 'in a flash' we realize that our consciousness and world is now 'illuminated', 'lit up' in a way that it wasn't before that moment. We are immersed, bathed in or filled with that light which is simply present in its dynamic, living way. We experience being in an 'enlightened' state, which does not mean we are being bombarded with waves or particles of anything coming from anywhere else.

Spiritual enlightenment would seem to mean an intuitive realizing of the unity of the cosmos, including our part in it at all levels of our being. This is a knowing beyond religious belief and beyond scientific proof.

The polar opposite of enlightenment would be what we might call 'endarkenment' – both individual and collective – an unavoidable fact of our incarnation in bodies of dense earthly matter, but also perhaps a result of our being kept 'in the dark' for whatever reasons.

And in this respect, as we realise how closely the Aether is identified with light, the expression "The brighter the light, the darker the shadows" takes on increasing significance.

From the polarity of light and darkness, we next consider an equally fundamental pair of cosmic polar opposites, **Levity** and **Gravity**.

Levity and Gravity

ENGINEER'S ASSUMPTION – The universal principle of *polarity* in the cosmos implies a complementary opposite to the contracting force we call *Gravity*. Such an opposite, expanding force would be working to return the cosmos to a state that existed prior to its cooling and solidifying into physical masses. That is, prior to *Gravity*.

KEY QUESTION – How do we think beyond Newton's and Einstein's descriptions of *Gravity*?

OVERVIEW

In this Report we can only touch briefly on *Gravity*, one of the fundamentals of the physical universe.

Sir Isaac Newton was the first Western scientist to identify it and put it on a scientific and mathematical basis.

As a man deeply interested and involved in spiritual and occult knowledge such as *alchemy*, he also covered a lot more ground than the Western science establishment has been prepared to acknowledge. And this included his writings on the polar opposite of *Gravity*, the universal expansive force, known in earlier times as *Levity*.

We can appreciate *Levity* directly when we see heat rising as in a flame or when we get a sense of elevation in our upright posture.

NT: You can have this notion of a force in the cosmos that's drawing away from the centre rather than towards it. And there's a lot of evidence that such a force exists in the cosmos

now. In fact 90% or more of the cosmos is supposed to consist of dark energy and dark matter.

It was around Newton's time that the *Accademia del Cimento* in Florence, then a world authority on scientific matters, issued a paper entitled *Contra Levitatem* which decreed that science should no longer recognize Levity as meriting equal rank with its opposite, *Gravity*.

The historical context was that of a newly emerging discipline of scientific enquiry which was trying to be ultra-objective, unlike religion, and focused solely on the physical, as opposed to anything which was reminiscent of mysticism or the Church. And the idea of *Levity*, as the opposite of *Gravity*, was felt to draw people away from a *physical* earthbound mentality towards a more transcendental, *aethereal* state.

At a stroke this denial of the principle of *polarity* prevented any <u>balanced</u> scientific enquiry into the nature of *Gravity*. And it helped distort Western science into making a false distinction between the *physical* – as what is 'real', and the *non-physical* – thereafter to be considered 'unreal' and so not worthy of scientific investigation.

So although, in its historical context, it can be seen to have had some justification its consequences have echoed on way beyond their useful time. For example, Western science's understanding of what 'force' is doesn't seem to have evolved much since then.

NT: **In physics we have the most naive conceptions of force only: namely, things hitting each other. And basically, what physicists have tried to do is to reduce all forces – the four fundamental forces of physics are reduced – to particles that hit each other. Basically.**

You have virtual photons that exchange momentum, when their exchange momentum is transferred. Well, basically you're back to things hitting each other.

The maths is sophisticated, the concepts are unthinkable but, if you boil it down to grass roots, it's things that hit each other. And that's all we've got for force. Nobody has any other description of force. If you ask a physicist what force is he can't tell you. He might produce some sophisticated maths. That's fine, Yes. But what actually is force?

What is a force? The only way I know what force is is from my own direct experience when I push on something. Now tell me – I mean, I know the answer but I'd like to hear your answer – How does physics describe force?

Back again with **Ian Thompson**, Professor of Physics.

ITh: It's a kind of hypothetical question in physics. Physics uses forces to answer hypothetical questions about, how would an object move if I put it there? How fast would it accelerate? If it had certain mass and there was a certain force there, how much would it accelerate? It would accelerate by $F \div M$ by Newton's Second Law. So they define it in this practical way, of saying what acceleration would result on a certain mass. And then force is calculated as the product of those two.

NT: Now tell me, do you think that that force is only hypothetical or does physics think that forces actually exist in some sense?

ITh: Well, this is a question which has much debate in physics and among the philosophers of science. I think most physicists, in their normal life, believe that there are potential fields. The gravitational energy of an object that's suspended up in space is present, even if it's not actually being used to accelerate it in a downward direction. And so.... that's what they normally believe. But if pressed, they become a little bit suspicious about this, because they don't really understand what this means.

So I think there are important questions to be answered in physics about forces, about energy. Ask a physicist what energy is – it's an ability to do work. Is there energy when work is not actually being done?

NT: And where do we get the concept of energy from? From our own experience again.

It was only in the mid-20th century that **Ernst Lehrs**, a writer and teacher qualified in electrical engineering, recovered the term *levity*, in his book *Man or Matter*. He wrote:

> *"Levity is a force polar to gravity. And because life is bound up with it, as death is bound up with gravity, it is recognised as being of more ancient rank than gravity.*
>
> *It must not be confused with the hypothetical 'anti-gravity'....*
>
> *Although capable of producing physical effects.... (levity) is itself of a non-physical nature."*

Even today scientists and others still speak of *gravity* and *anti-gravity* or *negative gravity* – that is, defining something by what it is not, as in the *horseless* carriage, and the *wireless*.

This avoiding of the name Levity is like speaking of *south as counter-north*, or *female as non-male* – as if *south* and *female* were taboo words.

The other outstanding figure in thinking about *Gravity*, apart from Newton, was **Albert Einstein**. By establishing that matter and energy are interchangeable, he helped liberate Physics from it's strictly mechanical view of Gravity.

But, lacking the polar opposite of gravity, ie *Levity*, his thinking became highly contrived, abstract and mathematical.

And when you're operating in that mode, you can make a case for just about anything that is conceivable – for example, ideas that have nothing whatsoever to do with the world we actually experience, so long as you make sure it's all mathematically consistent.

In this respect, it's significant how Einstein needed to think up various totally unreal *mind experiments* – about all sorts of physically impossible situations – but then keep these well apart from his mathematical formulations.

His theories also assume an absolutely constant 'speed or velocity of light' throughout the universe – something very much disputed by Nick Thomas and others.

Consequently, *Relativity Theory* ended up leaving its believers adrift, without any sense of meaning or purpose – without a cosmic context to relate to.

That means you can only see yourself relative to other similarly disconnected physical objects adrift in spacetime.

For his so-called 'cosmological constant' was no more than an abstract mathematical device for balancing an equation.

NT: **Now what the cosmological constant brings into Relativity is the possibility of a levity-like mode of action in the whole cosmos, in contradistinction to gravity. Relativity explains, <u>in a very abstract way</u>, the truth.**
The truth is <u>not</u> abstract; the truth involves Aether, it involves consciousness. But you can describe that same truth with very abstract mathematics. And that's what Relativity does.

Yet, to the end, he still intuitively affirmed the existence of a non-material *Aether*, while paradoxically excluding it from his long running but vain attempts to come up with a grand unifying theory.

To summarise: *Gravity* and *Levity* are the names given to the two complementary polar forces always in dynamic relationship which govern the cosmos.

Gravity is the drawing *inwards* from the whole cosmos towards any point in it; and *Levity* is the drawing *outwards* from any point into the wider cosmos.

To deny either of these would be to deny ourselves any realistic chance of understanding how this universe came to be and how it functions as a whole system.

An investigating engineer needs as much of the whole picture as he or she can get.

Nick Thomas has presented <u>his</u> interpretation of *Gravity* as a dynamic stress relationship created between the *aethereal* and the *physical* dimensions. He has developed a mathematically precise way to demonstrate this, using geometrical diagrams of a special kind. And it matches up exactly with Newton's formula for Gravity.

It also enables us to understand *magnetism* and *electricity* – as resulting from the interplay of the two forces, *Gravity* and *Levity*: magnetism the more *earthbound* and electricity the more *aethereal*.

NT: Now, one of the forces which interested me all my life from the age of, I don't know what – four or something – was gravity. I basically always had a longing to discover anti-gravity. Anyway I was always terribly interested in gravity and I thought to myself straight away, 'Ah, gravity. We don't know what gravity is. Nobody does.'

Sir Isaac Newton brilliantly descibed it with an exact formula. Einstein brought some very clever modifications, very far-reaching modifications, to that but neither of those two gentlemen actually explained gravity. They only descibed it.

Newton to the end of his life was anxious about this 'action at a distance', this force that acted from one thing to another with nothing in between. There's no levers, rods, elastic bands, nothing, you know? For Newton this was a horror, but he couldn't get round it.

So I thought to myself, Ah, here's a good candidate. Suppose gravity is stress in counterspace? Why not? So I thought, Well if this works, the whole thing's worth going on with. And if it doesn't, I'll abandon it.

I then applied a little bit of nifty maths and came up with the most horrendous equation. And I looked at this and I thought, God, that's nothing like gravity. It had arc tangents in it and I don't know what else. And I looked at this thing....

But being a persistent individual I thought to myself that I must at least finish this off. I'll just stick the boundary conditions in and see what I actually get. So I stuck the boundary conditions in .... and the equation collapsed into Newton's Law!

And I sat there actually in a state of shock. I was looking at the paper and thought, 'Crikey!', you know? Here it actually was. It worked. The idea made sense, not just as a thought or an idea, but it actually produces the correct formula.

THE ENGINEER'S 3 TESTS

- regarding Western science and Gravity

TEST 1: SOUND PRINCIPLES?

Trying to understand Gravity without taking into account its cosmic polar opposite, Levity, is a one-sided and therefore *unsound*, unscientific approach.

In several vain attempts to remedy the situation, various less than convincing fixes have been proposd. For example, the highly speculative and completely indescribable *dark matter* and *dark energy*.

Dark matter is supposed to make up 'the difference', that is, the 'missing' gravity – which is sought because the current physics dogma about mass and gravity doesn't seem to fit what's being observed and measured in the wider cosmos. And *dark energy* has been proposed to make up for the missing expansive, counter-gravitational principle in the universe – that is, so long as *Levity* remains taboo.

And physicists, in their obsession with the idea of particles, are also now seeking some imaginary 'particles of gravity' which they're referring to as *gravitons*.

TEST 2: ELEGANT DESIGN?

There's little sign of elegance when the best substitutes that can be found for the missing *Levity* are what-it's-not ideas like *anti-gravity* and *dark energy*.

TEST 3: EFFICIENT OPERATION?

Although workable within limited situations, the anomalies arising from Western science's denial of *Levity* make its version of *Gravity* an unbalanced and therefore inefficient system of thought.

Yet simply reinstating the principle of Levity could instantly clarify and transform Western science's thinking about space, time and the whole subject of forces in the cosmos, including Gravity.

We could then dispense with some of Einstein's impossible mind-experiments and translate his highly abtract ideas into more realistic concepts.

In the following section, we address two areas of science, **Quantum Physics** and **Chaos Theory**, which themselves represent two almost polar opposite approaches. Together they epitomize the crisis point Western science has reached and the choice of direction it faces right now.

Quantum

NT: We talk about crossing a threshold, in a way. It's a threshold of consciousness. You can imagine it: you're moving from one kind of consciousness and you're going to turn that consciousness inside out. And it's like coming up to a dark wall and going beyond it and hoping you're going to wake up on the other side. And when you do wake up on the other side you wake up then with this completely different viewpoint.

If you do that, you are involved as an individual. You're not looking at it as an onlooker. <u>You're there</u>. And this goes back to our previous question – a lot of people want to <u>be there</u>. They don't just want to sit outside and look. And what Einstein, Pauli, Heisenberg, those pioneering Quantum Physics, they were still trying to use the kind of consciousness which sits back like an island and looks at what's happening <u>out there</u>, objectively. They wanted to do that. And they succeeded in reaching across that boundary I'm talking about, that threshold. They reached across it using powerful and very esoteric equipment. And we're still doing that.

And so what they're really trying to do is to, instead of changing their consciousness, they're trying to get the goods from the other side, as it were, without changing their consciousness. And they've been very successful at doing it. There's one catch. When you do that the results are nearly always destructive.

If you're not personally <u>there</u>, then you have no control over what's happening <u>there</u>. And that's why the first result of their efforts was an atom bomb. Because the results tend to be destructive.

And our big challenge therefore is to not do it the way Einstein and Pauli did, which is to try and stay back in our ordinary consciousness, but to go there, be there, be responsible.

ENGINEER'S ASSUMPTION – The word 'Quantum' is bandied about as if most of us have a definite idea of what it means – when in fact we don't at all. And similarly with the word 'particle', as used in Particle Physics, a branch of Quantum Physics.

Richard Feynmam, Nobel laureate and physicist, said famously: "*I think it is safe to say that no-one understands quantum physics.*"

KEY QUESTION – What is the reality behind the various anomalies and paradoxes collectively known as *Quantum Physics*?

OVERVIEW

At the beginning of the 20th century, Western science, with its powerful new microscopes penetrating ever deeper into the secrets of matter, passed through a critical stage when the *Quantum* idea was introduced.

In the broader social context, human consciousness was evolving into increasing individuality.

In Physics this was an era of *analysing* – that is, endlessly dividing up, separating and excluding – as opposed to *synthesizing*, which is about including and combining.

And among physicists, there was an obsessive quest to detect the smallest possible particle of matter – in order to establish what might be the so-called 'building blocks' of the universe.

In this context, a theory arose, stating that energy comes, not in a continuous flow, but in tiny, separate packages or quantities. Hence the word *quantum* for each of these unimaginably small units of energy.

Some sixty years later, however, it was again **Richard Feynman** who rather undermined this whole idea, saying: *"Science fails to admit that it has not the slightest clue what energy is."*

In simple terms, the *quantum* idea, put an artificial lower limit on 'smallness'. It said that below a certain microscopic scale there can be no further measurement. Whatever exists below that scale must be continuous, ie <u>not</u> consisting of separate bits.

So it effectively served as a kind of limit beyond which there could be no more *quanti*-fying.

This was a kind of follow-up to Western science's earlier corruption of the word *atom*, which actually means an *indivisible entity*. That makes the word *sub-atomic* meaningless, unless you think of atoms as some kind of physical objects – obviously <u>not</u> then indivisible.

NT: When we bring some ideas of the Aether to this situation the whole picture can become much clearer. The Aether is related to the physical in quite an interesting way in that, in its own realm, it isn't necessarily quantifiable – certainly not in physical terms. But when it relates as it were, connects, to the physical, then it crosses, one could say, a sort of threshold, in a way. It crosses over into a definite form and thereby becomes quantifiable. And of course, on going the other way – if one goes back out of physical space again – that quantifiable aspect is lost again.

And it can help perhaps to have an analogy here (although it's not very exact, it at least gives a picture) and that is, that if you cool water below a certain temperature then tangible pieces of ice come into existence – little solid bits. And of course, if the temperature's raised again above the freezing level, these bits of ice gradually cease to exist.

As far as Heisenberg's Uncertainty Principle is concerned, an important aspect of quantum physics, this says that there's a limit to the accuracy with which any process or any action can be measured. And that again is very very interesting because the way the threshold exists, the way the Aether and the physical relate to one another, beautifully describes why there should be an Uncertainty Principle. Because it does depend on how you bring the two into relationship.

In the bigger picture, then, the *quantum* idea can be seen as an early, although unintentional, move towards marking out the critical boundary between:

(a)   the *physical* world of measurable units of matter, ie particles etc, and

(b)   another realm beyond this, where *continuity* rules in the form of *continuous flowing* movement, ie the *Aether*.

And so we now have *polarity*, and a choice of perspectives, depending on which side of that boundary we put ourselves as observers: the *aethereal* or the *physical*.

The emergence of the *Quantum* idea in Physics was part of a much broader rebalancing in human consciousness, which would eventually mark the end of an era of *masculine* dominance.

In the first half of the 20th century, Aether denial was the norm amongst physicists. And when we look at the highly intellectual, masculine kind of mentality that dominated Western science then, in the early days of *nuclear fission* research, a very unappealing picture presents itself.

We see a boylike poke-it-and-see curiosity – which was not only immature, but actually encouraged. Consequently, certain actions followed which amounted to a high-tech *rape of Nature*. That is, the forceful penetrating and injecting of potent material into the entities called 'atoms'.

The so-called 'splitting of the atom' can also be seen as a crude, artificial attempt at *alchemy* – again without acknowledging the Aether – but with the physicists trying to dominate Nature and bring forth new forms of matter in an arbitrary, godlike manner. They were playing with aethereal forces of a potency way beyond their appreciation.

And not surprisingly, these activities released huge amounts of both instant, explosive energy and long term radiating energy – of an intensity most organic life on Earth cannot withstand.

Being of a fundamentally different order from physical or chemical hazards, this deadly energy invisibly, silently, odourlessly disintegrates living tissue. 'Radiation sickness', is the unspoken dark side of the claim that nuclear energy is 'clean' (in that it produces relatively little carbon).

And so through the now worldwide nuclear energy industry, we have ever increasing quantities of deadly radioactive material – predicted to remain so for thousands of years – which no one knows how to dispose of safely and which will always present a major security risk.

Currently in the UK a new attempt is being made to justify more nuclear technology. The claim is being made, based on particular statistics, that a low level intake of radiation, is not harmful. So there's no reason for anyone to feel negative about nuclear power generators.

The fundamental flaw – or perhaps deceit – in this thinking is in reducing everything to quantities. So that, in this case, different kinds of radiation, naturally occurring and artificially provoked, are all treated as if they're identical.

They are then precisely measured in standard units... of intensity.

This is as inadequate as assessing the emanation of fragrance or sound only in terms of its intensity or volume, ie as a quantity. It completely ignores the inherent variations of quality which, in the case of radiation, would be due to the unique combination of geological and other factors in each situation

Engineer Nick Thomas has a very pragmatic view of this confused and politically very loaded situation – bearing in mind Western science's unawareness of what it's actually dealing with, which is the Aether.

NT: The problem with nuclear power to my mind is not that we shouldn't do it, it's that we should do it only when we know how to. And there are a number of unknowns, let's say, at the moment. We don't really know the effect of low-level radiation over a long period. We haven't got the least clue how to deal with radioactive waste – and the argument goes on as to whether it should be buried deep, buried shallow or buried intermediate. And there are different arguments for those so called solutions.

The best solution from some people's point of view would be to send it into space, but who's going to risk a rocket blowing up on take-off full of radioactive waste? How do you deal with waste products? Will we ever be able to find a new physics that can handle those waste products?

It's certainly something which I'm hoping to come up with, with the help of this Aetheric science which we've been speaking about.

I think, 'if the current physics can't solve the problem then we need a new physics' is a bit of a cavalier way of saying it, but I

think it's true.

As evolution goes forward we'll be handling more and more dangerous things, much more dangerous actually than radioactivity, and what is important is not to shy away from what's dangerous but it's to handle it properly, responsibly. Know how to handle it before launching into a huge project.

Meanwhile, in the current manoeuvrings about whether to commission new nuclear energy generators, certain fundamental questions seem to have been completely ignored. For example, concerning the so-called 'energy gap', this supposedly ever increasing need for electric power can be seen as the direct result of an artificially hyped up worldwide demand... for non-essential goods and services. But that's not the business of this Report.

It's significant how ignorance of the Aether, combined with naïve curiosity, made the early nuclear physicists so easily exploitable – whether as willing or reluctant collaborators.

And currently, we have genetic engineering continuing the 'poke-it-and-see' tradition with a disrespectful forcible penetrating of living membranes, nature's boundaries, in order to inject alien substance into 'victim' cells.

Meanwhile, the probing, penetrating physicists – almost exclusively male – had, so to speak, passed right through the vanishing point at the centre of the physical world, and unknowingly, were now well into the dimension of the *Aether.* However, this is governed by principles the <u>polar opposite</u> of those applying in the physical world – which made the whole venture extremely challenging for them.

Werner Heisenberg, the famous German physicist and Quantum pioneer, said: *"Can Nature possibly be as absurd as it seems to us in these atomic experiments?"*

Unwittingly 'progressing backwards', without a clue as to where they were or might be heading, they continued to use the language of the physical-material world. That is, they kept trying to *quantify* their way through the non-*quantifiable*, non-material *Aether*.

Hence the unlikely name, *Quantum Mechanics* – given the lack of anything *mechanical* there, in the normal sense of the word. And hence the many puzzling paradoxes which inevitably resulted from applying an old, inappropriate mindset to a new and radically different set of circumstances.

NT: So since the 1930s we've known perfectly well that physics cannot explain anything. *That* we know.

        When Quantum Physics was first being developed it was very difficult to understand. Even Einstein said at the time that they felt as if the rug was being pulled out from under them. And Pauli, one of the great physicists of the twentieth century, a brilliant man – he said he wished he'd been a movie comedian or something. Anything rather than a physicist – it's so difficult.

It's important to remember that the *Quantum* idea is basically no more than that – an *idea*. It does not indicate a separately existing 'something', an entity in itself.

NT: What first arose in physics was the notion, strange notion, that you can break the laws of physics as long as you do it for a very short time.

        It's rather like, you can get away with speeding providing you do it between the speed cameras. You can get away with breaking the laws of physics, you can create energy out of nothing, as long as you only do it for a very short time and let it vanish again. Because there was evidence in experiments with bubble-chambers, cloud-chambers, those kinds of experiments where things are supposed to fly through and leave their tracks, and their very complex tracks are there. And evidence starts to accrue that there are events going on which aren't normal. Events which are happening, you know, between the speed-cameras.

And eventually this idea, that such events occur, was forced upon scientists and they were able to 'give leave' to these events with the aid of something called Heisenberg's Uncertainty Principle. It was realised that the degree of certainty you can impose on the world is limited. And at an everyday level.... there's little doubt about where that computer is .... it isn't sort of statistically located somewhere in this room. And when you say, 'I want to turn the computer on', I have to, sort of, fix my consciousness to a point when it will graciously agree to appear to be here and I can work with it.

Fortunately, in the everyday world things aren't like that. Whereas down at the sub-atomic realm that's just what they're like. And if you want to locate where an electron is you have to somehow get it to graciously appear, here, if it will. And this is rather difficult to do.

Now, what was realised is that this 'graciousness', that may or may not be there, is what lies between the speed-cameras, you see. And so you can then turn it round and exploit it. And you can say, 'Ah! While it's not looking, while it's turned its back, we'll have something come into existence.' And it creates a bubble and then it vanishes again.

And so this.... quantum fluctuations, fluctuations in the vacuum, Zero Point energy – the different names for it.... this idea was born in physics, it's possible according to the laws of physics and it's now thought that it actually must happen. Because there are certain things, certain very sensitive experiments, that lend support to the notion.

And before you know where you are, you're back with an Aether again, but a completely different conception from that of the Nineteenth Century. You're back with the notion of a seething bubbling interface at the ground level of the world.

And you don't have vacuum any more – there's always something going on there. And you might as well call it Aether. Why not?

And so, in a sense, it's risen up again. It's not the Aether we're thinking of when we speak about the aethereal. But I believe actually that those experiments, those phenomena that have given rise to it are themselves the bubbling of the Aether, but not in the way it's envisaged in physics.

I think something is indeed going on at the interface between, if you like, our world and another, but instead of materialising it in that way, into little material particles coming into existence and vanishing again, it needs to be re-thought in terms of a stress boundary between the two worlds.

And in 2001, professor of physics and science writer, Paul Davies, proposed the acknowledgement of what he called a 'quantum ether'.

Two of the Quantum paradoxes, still unresolved in Physics today, are:

Nonlocality: which says that particles can be everywhere and anywhere at once, and

Superposition: which says that a particle exists in more than one state until it's observed, at which moment one of them is established as its current state.

Regarding nonlocality, physicist Yakir Aharanov is quoted as saying that scientists deal with this apparent anomaly **'by**

not thinking about it'.

Both of these Quantum paradoxes imply a state of universal presence – more like a state of mind than of matter. These obviously require a dimension beyond our normal physical space and time, ie a more subtle medium that permeates all the bits and pieces of the material-physical world. And one name for this in the Western world has long been the Aether.

Here's **Nick Thomas** with professor of Physics, **Ian Thompson,** clarifying what they do and don't mean by the Aether in this discussion.

ITh: So you think that there's something intrinsically non-local about the Aether? You have an idea of the Aether which is very different from the ideas that have been entertained by the physicists, whether it's a nineteenth century ether of a perfectly.... very stiff, elastic solid, or whether it's Quantum Physics' ether which is all the 'zero point energy', or whether it's the modern Aether of 'dark matter'. All of these ideas of the Aether are not wholistic. They think of them as something of the Aether, which can be divided. You can take the Aether in one part of space and separate it from the Aether in another part of space.

So you think there's a different kind of Aether present, which has non-local properties?

NT: Yes, and to take the 'zero point energy' that you spoke about. It's very interesting. I'm coming to the view, especially with some recent work I've been doing in the last couple of weeks, that 'zero point action' if you like, if one could call it that, the actions that are going on – particles popping into existence and vanishing again, as long as Heisenberg is respected, as it were – that is actually an interface between the two kinds of

space. It isn't the Aether, but it 's an <u>interface</u> between the physical and the Aether. That's how it's seeming to me at the moment.

Now, at the beginning of the 21st century, **Roger Penrose** and other scientists are expressing profound doubts about Physics itself, which simply cannot resolve these fundamental paradoxes it has created.

A further major paradox is the incompatibility between the theories of the large scale, such as *Gravity*, and those of the subatomic *Quantum* scale.

From the detached perspective of an investigating engineer, this particular dilemma is the result of trying to weld together two gross misconceptions of contemporary Physics. First, Gravity – without its polar opposite Levity; and second, the Quantum realm, wrongly conceived as a result of mistakenly looking into the aethereal realm as if it were physical and therefore quantifiable.

Currently there is some experimental research being done by physicists aiming to find the scale or level at which the so called Quantum laws 'break down' (as they say) and the physical laws to do with Gravity come into play.

But seen differently, it's another case of science progressing 'backwards'. For what the physicists are actually seeking here – perhaps unknowingly – is the critical boundary between the physical and the aethereal. And so we're back with the much needed bridge in Western scientific thinking, which Nick Thomas has been building for some time.

Again, from an engineering perspective, it would be much more scientifically sound if the Quantum idea, with all its misconceptions and resulting paradoxes, were to be quietly discarded, and Levity were reinstated as the polar opposite of Gravity.

Then Western science could make a fresh start to the 21st century, cleared of all the confusing Quantum dogma it's been lumbered with for so long.

Penrose openly speaks of the need for, and indeed his expectation of, an imminent revolution in this area. And, as if in response, the essential message of this Engineer's Report is that the revolution is here now – for those with the eyes to see and the ears to hear.

One indicator of the power of the Aether is what's known as atomic or nuclear energy, ie that which is released through a destructive atom-splitting process. However, given the inherent polarity of the cosmos, there is also a creative potential in the Aether – equally powerful and exploitable for good or evil.

This creative aspect works on the more subtle level of ideas and communication. And, crucially, it's not accessible through the ways of materialistic science.

It requires a very different approach, based on principles we normally understand as morals and ethics – or human values. That's because the aethereal level is essentially an indivisible oneness, and therefore the thoughts and deeds of each individual in it affect every other individual in it. So the morality is a kind of inescapable responsibility involving everyone.

Western science has already become used to the extraordinary at the so-called Quantum level of reality. So perhaps this requirement may not seem as outrageous now as it would have done at the beginning of the 20th century.

And one possible conclusion from all this is that the whole Quantum enterprise has been a false trail, a cul de sac, a dead end. For at the sub-atomic, aethereal level, there are no discrete quantum units of anything, no quantum objects at all... but plenty of physicists desperately trying to imagine that blips on a screen represent actual objects.

Meanwhile, stepping back from the detail and thinking more laterally, the inquisitive engineer asks:

Do I take the 'fact of life', affirmed by physicists, that the observer affects and changes whatever he or she is observing, as just one more quirk in the strange world of Quantum Physics? ... OR do I take it, alternatively, as an inspiring revelation?

For what it tells us is that we are continuously affecting our world, ourselves and others, with our minds at a very subtle level – according to our attitudes, hidden assumptions and intentions. This realization, combined with superposition and nonlocality, gives us a clue to such mysteries as healing, telepathy, synchronicity and hypnosis.

Such implications are officially ignored by the Western science establishment, which is still trying to hold on to the unrealistic ideal of objectivity in science.

However, if taken on board positively, it seems likely that these implications could quickly transform public attitudes towards science and scientists: from indifference, mistrust and hostility to an enthusiastic fascination.

Which goes some way towards answering the main brief of this Report, Why is Western science such a turn-off for so many people?

THE ENGINEER'S 3 TESTS

– regarding Western science and Quantum Physics

TEST 1: SOUND PRINCIPLES?

In the early 20th century, Western science abandoned any idea of an aether existing. Instead it established the *Quantum* idea – by misinterpreting how, at the threshold between these two realms, *aethereal* processes become *physical* and thereby *quantifiable*.

NT: I think, actually, Quantum Physics will only be understood when we understand this concept, Aether. All that Quantum Physics wrestles with to do with the wholistics aspects of the universe, which it does wrestle with – for instance it has a wave equation which it thinks relates to the whole cosmos; it has non-locality, because it's quite clear, and there is experimental evidence for it, that there are non-local connections between things in the universe. And yet the comfortable, cosy physics, 'action by touch', doesn't work for those kind of concepts.

One is trying to bring in concepts which involve non-locality, relationship of the whole to the part, which our traditional, scientific concepts cannot embrace. The Aether can. The Aether is precisely the polar opposite of locality. The Aether is precisely cosmic. That doesn't mean it's not concerned with locality. The Aether is continuously being concerned with the relationship between what is cosmic, peripheral, total and what is local and finite.

And Life Aether in particular, is that which mediates these two.

And so that's what lies behind my position with regard to the Aether.

TEST 2: ELEGANT DESIGN?

The early 20th century was a very inelegant, fraught, messy and confusing time in Physics, heightened by the wider political context of fiercely competing national governments and scientists – and in a situation of looming and then ongoing war. Since then, the misconceptions emerging from that stressful atmosphere have become a kind of dogma of anomalies and paradoxes, leaving present day Physics sadly lacking in both coherence and *elegance*.

TEST 3: EFFICIENT OPERATION?

With much official secrecy, many fundamental differences and various bitter rivalries going on, *efficient in operation* is one thing the early Quantum scene was not. Except perhaps in that the awesome, deadly power of nuclear fission was over-hurriedly rushed into an ill-prepared world.

And so it has continued into the present, as humanity tries to deal with the many complicated and deadly consequences of those events.

To quote an old, practical maxim: *If you've dug yourself too deeply into a hole and can't get out, first, stop digging.*

To realize and acknowledge that the so-called Quantum realm is actually a misconceived view of the *Aether* would be a very positive and healing step forward for Western science. It would also surely make Physics and Western science as a whole a lot more accessible and appealing.

Chaos Theory, in the next section, can be seen as a much needed polar opposite – to counterbalance what modern Physics has become. Then we begin to see that **Chaos** and the misunderstood *Quantum* world are in fact intimately related.

Chaos and Cosmos

NT: When Chaos Theory came along I was absolutely thrilled because it completely broke open this notion of a closed mechanical system

ENGINEER'S ASSUMPTION – What may seem random and unpredictable to limited <u>human</u> understanding may well appear orderly and predictable to a more advanced consciousness. And conversely, an outwardly ordered situation may be composed of many unpredictable processes.

KEY QUESTION – How can we achieve a more wholistic and balanced understanding of the polarity between what we call order and disorder?

OVERVIEW

Looking back, *Chaos Theory* seemed to arrive in the 1970s as a kind of antidote to the *masculine* ethos dominating Western science. *Chaos* is an ancient Greek word which refers to a womb-like, seething realm of living energy or potential, before this has been formed into an *order* we recognise.

And this description bears more than a passing resemblance to such modern ideas as the so called *Quantum Vacuum* and *Zero Point Field*. For both of these can be seen as limited, compromised views of the dynamic interface between the *physical* and the *aethereal* – as seen from the <u>physical</u> side.

The polar opposite of chaos is *cosmos*, another Greek word, which means *order*.

We can recognize *chaos* in the turbulence of transformation we find at the *threshold* between one level of order and another – for example, where boiling water is transforming into vapour.

'There's method in my madness' is a familiar expression which says there's order within this apparent *disorder*.

And we're familiar with stories of how seemingly insignificant events lead to unpredicted outcomes, sometimes momentous. These put the essential ideas of *Chaos Theory* in a familiar, everyday setting.

Chaos Theory includes such characteristic features as:

Non-predictability – which is due to *disorder* at the micro-level underlying a superficial *order* at the larger scale. It means that any long term predicting based on present circumstances is unreliable, however seemingly predictable the short term may be. This realisation arose out of scientific and mathematical attempts to predict the weather.

Then there's _Non-linearity_ – which means that instead of looking for *lines* or chains of causes and effects, linked in a mechanical way, we see the consequences of any event rippling outwards in all directions.

The Butterfly Effect is a term for the way in which tiny events can have enormous consequences if the ripples build up into big waves.

And fourth, there are _Fractals_ – which reveal, in apparently *random* or *disorderly* situations, a hidden inner *order* of repetitive patterning, as we go down and down in scale. This is normally demonstrated by computer graphics which can powerfully magnify one detail of an image, revealing an exact replica, and so on, infinitely 'inwards'.

NT: Chaos was a discovery, or a development, which excited me enormously because, as an engineer, I was very concerned that one thinks things through consistently, and all that we'd been taught and all that one was understanding at the time of this universe made it seem as if it were this giant mechanism. And

Chaos Theory destroyed that view utterly. Because I knew it wasn't a giant mechanism.

So when Chaos Theory came along I was absolutely thrilled because it completely broke open this notion of a closed mechanical system – it is a lie now to perpetrate it. Before, it was a misunderstanding; with the discovery of Chaos Theory it's become a lie. People sometimes still promote it, in which case they're lying, now, in the face of Chaos Theory – to put it quite bluntly.

Now, what it does is, it makes it then conceivable that there is an interface between – or a 'oneness' of the mixture of – what we call physical and what one talks about as the Aetheric. They're part and parcel of each other. One doesn't want to be dualistic – I'm not thinking of a marionette being pulled by Aether strings. I think that would be a misconception. Rather, it now makes sense that these fine, delicate processes as they appear to us – but actually very powerful processes that are Aetheric processes – can interface with the very powerful mechanical processes we think of as making up the physical world. There is a possible interface between the two.

Chaos Theory, if you like, enables one to think how that's possible. It enables one to see that the physical is not a closed system and therefore something else can be part of the loop, namely the Aether. That's to put it in very simple terms.

So from our overview, *Chaos Theory* can be seen as a much needed follow-up to *Quantum Physics*, to counterbalance at least some of the distorted and confused thinking which arose from the *quantum* idea.

And, at the subtle, micro-level, various correspondences between the worlds of Chaos and Quantum can be seen – since they are essentially two different but limited views of the Aether.

They are both addressing a wholly different order from that of the *physical-material* world, an order that prevails beyond the threshold of *smallness*. The trouble is that they're only doing it from the *physical* side, thinking only in *physical* terms, and using equipment designed to detect only *physical* phenomena.

It's a bit like looking at the sky through a grid, and concluding that the sky must be made up of a patchwork of separate squares.

Also, we become aware of the negative what-it's-not terminology in each:

In Chaos Theory we have *nonlinearity* and in Quantum Mechanics *nonlocality*, both indicating a kind of total *continuity*... or *wholeness*.

In Chaos Theory there's *non-predictability* and in Quantum Mechanics the *Uncertainty Principle* – each reminding us how meaningless it is to think about the *Aether* in *physical* terms.

These factors would account for the highly contrived, double-negative thinking found in the new sub-branch of physics called Quantum Chaology. For example, *"...the quantum suppression of chaos is itself suppressed by decoherence..."* to quote a recent publication.

Chaos Theory has never been welcomed by the mainstream orthodoxy of Western science. Presumably this has been because it seems to undermine a traditionally masculine set up. And the non-specialist, cross-disciplinary approach required by chaos thinking threatens to disturb an otherwise chronically compartmentalised world.

Thus we might expect Western science to try and sideline Chaos Theory – possibly by absorbing it and then relabeling it as, say, *Complexity Theory*, which sounds more like a minor backwater of mainstream Western science.

However, what *Chaos Theory* has brought us is far too important and needed for it to be quietly ignored.

So, one way or another, under one name or another it will necessarily reassert itself.

One of the pioneers of Chaos Theory, **Mitchell Feigenbaum**, remarked that it *'completely changed what it means to know something'* – in the sense of how problems are tackled in Physics.

THE ENGINEER'S 3 TESTS

– regarding Western science and Chaos Theory

TEST 1: SOUND PRINCIPLES?

Chaos Theory has begun to base Western science's thinking about order and disorder, and predictability on sound principles.

TEST 2: ELEGANT DESIGN?

Chaos Theory does bring some elegance to this area of Western science – in the sense that it more truly reflects what actually happens in Nature at critical stages of its processes, and how limited our control over Nature really is in the longer term.

TEST 3: EFFICIENT OPERATION?

The applications of Chaos Theory do demonstrably work, and provide a much deeper understanding of various principles behind Nature's workings. This should result in greater efficiency, that is, if the necessary resources are put into Chaos research.

The idea of *Chaos* as the creative and formative, but apparently disorderly activity of Nature, is a key to making sense of the so-called 'random mutations' of Charles Darwin's famous theory, our next subject: **Evolution**.

Evolution and Involution

NT: I think Darwinian Theory is flawed, but the question is not whether Darwinism works, the question is, Did we arise like that?

ENGINEER'S ASSUMPTIONS

This subject raises some of the deepest questions we can ask about our human existence:

Who are we? How did we come to be here? and *How did we come to be the way we are now?*

However, addressing these questions in a clear-minded way is made all the more difficult by a long-running divisive conflict. That is, the dispute between those religious fundamentalists known as creationists, who take the biblical 'Seven Days' story literally, and those materialists, known as evolutionists, who deny any kind of purposeful creative processes driving Nature. This futile and distracting conflict can be and needs to be transcended. For there is a more mature, wholistic approach which reaches way beyond such limited alternatives, both of which are based on fear.

The materialists fear a return to worldwide domination by religious organizations, given the Church's history of dogmatic and cruel suppression of freethinking.

The creationists, meanwhile, fear a 'value-free', secular world culture, one which denies any purpose or design behind Nature by reducing it to a series of random events, and teaches that life itself arose spontaneously from non-living matter.

We can now apply a little reverse engineering to understand how the present situation was reached:

My journey from home to work could be analysed as a sequence of steps which add up to the particular route I took, with the result that I somehow happened to arrive at my workplace. This is the materialistic view, which completely excludes one crucial factor: I intentionally made that journey. That's what gives the whole process coherence.

On the other hand it does seem totally unbelievable that the wondrous garden that is this planet was delivered complete and up-and-running in six days flat. Almost like a TV gardening makeover.

However, this does not rule out reading, say, the Old Testament of the Bible as an encoded record of real processes unfolding over long periods of time.

The transcendent view is that we are all parts of an evolving creative process AND a creatively evolving process. This follows from appreciating how the principle of 'polarity within wholeness' plays out in human affairs.

KEY QUESTION – How did Western science become so committed to a deeply flawed view (1) of humankind's place in the order of Nature, and (2) of life itself and how it regenerates?

OVERVIEW

The conflict between the creationists and the evolutionists looks, to an unbiased engineer, like a cleverly engineered set-up for sabotaging a system – that is, for neutralizing its energy and power by directing two significant forces within it against one another.

In politics, this is known as the divide-and-rule technique. And regarding the study of evolution, one of the effects of such a set-up would be to distract minds from true scientific enquiry.

For when we see our planet as viewed from space, these petty divisions seem shallow and misguided.

This continuing re-enactment of a long outdated battle is an irrelevant distraction. We see both sides more concerned with defending their own positions than with seeking any deeper understanding of humanity's place in Nature and the cosmos. It's more about politics than science or spirituality.

In Western science, two major misconceptions have resulted from all this. First, the false conclusion has been reached that humankind is the end product of a selective breeding process – somewhat like, but on a grander scale than, the highly bred homing pigeons **Charles Darwin** himself studied.

And, second, going further back, the idea that life on Earth arose 'spontaneously' from non-living matter, that is, from a primordial soup of chemicals. Attempts to come up with a recipe for this in the laboratory, however, still remain purely speculative.

NT: As far as the 'primordial soup' is concerned: Did life arise in a 'primordial soup'? Looked at from an Aetheric perspective, the answer's, No. Because life existed before matter existed. And therefore it certainly didn't arise from a primordial soup. On the other hand, looked at from a physical perspective – if you put on your physical lenses, as everybody has done at the moment, and only look at the earth as a physical object – then of course, at some time or other in the past this physical substance suddenly appeared, or anyway, became, over whatever timescale, organised into what we would call life. And somebody might think of that as a primordial soup or whatever. And one can't argue with that. It just leaves out the fact that the agency that was organising it was not lightning, as is imagined, or electric discharges, Experiments have been done, where for instance a guess has been made at what the primordial soup was like and then powerful electric sparks, really powerful ones, have been passed through this primordial soup – 'Ooh look! Hey! Bingo! There's some self-organised matter arising. <u>That's</u> how it arose.'

The fallacy of that is two-fold. One, of course, is the assumption of what the 'primordial soup' was like. (But you know one can't be too hard on that – one has to make assumptions to move on.)

But the much more understandable assumption is that matter today is exactly the same as matter was millions of years ago. And of course today matter actually, from an Aetheric perspective, has itself evolved. So today you have matter superbly tuned to... life.

An explanation is, that the whole way matter is structured, what matter is – the sort of enzymes you can have, the sort of structures they can take on, the fine tuning of the physical constants (such as Fred Hoyle should have won a Nobel Prize for) – these sort of things aren't there as accidents. Everybody recognises it but not many people will admit it. But they're not there as accidents.

It's quite clear, the system has evolved. Current matter, physics, the energy levels of the atoms, right up to the high level uranium ones and beyond – they're not there as an accident. The whole thing's evolved. With life. With the Aether. In fact really they are part and parcel... the Aether and those things go together.

A lot of what we describe as physical isn't. It's Aetheric. It's just that we use complex maths instead of the Aether to describe it, and think that we understand something. Well, we understand the structure but we don't understand the content at all.

So you see that's the most devastatingly wrong conception

about the 'primordial soup', because you take something that's evolved now and you translate it back to that time, as if it was there then, when it wasn't. So that's the 'primordial soup'.

Now, Darwin himself produced a theory of Natural Selection which, as a mechanism, works. I mean, for instance we evolve electronic circuits using this mechanism. And they evolve circuits much quicker than we can work them out ourselves. And there have been some stunning examples of complex circuits that have been evolved 'genetically', as it's now called. There's 'genetic' development of computer programmes, 'genetic' development of circuits and things. It's pure Darwinism and it works beautifully.

So the question is not whether Darwinism works, the question is, Did we arise like that? And the answer to that is, No.

Now that's a bald statement, but you see the reason the answer's No is for the reason I was just talking about with the primordial soup – we've come about through evolution of a different kind. Not an evolution that's based on a mechanical selection process but in fact this wonderful symbiosis between the Aether and the physical, where the two have developed and grown together. And that's why one can only look at the living world with wonder.

And Darwin's theory of *natural selection* does not, of course, answer the obvious questions:

How was the selecting programme set up in the first place, and for what purpose, since the very process of selecting implies some pre-set guiding principles for making choices?

He described the actual origin of species as 'the mystery of mysteries'.

And it's significant that Darwin himself wrote that he used the expression 'natural selection' – which implies Nature *purposefully* choosing – only as a *metaphor*. As a metaphor for what or who doing what is not made clear at all.

Yet Western science continues to proclaim that there is an unbroken chain of *heredity* connecting humankind with apes of an earlier time – which would make them our direct, bloodline ancestors. And this despite the fact that there have been questions all along about the so-called 'missing link' between apes and humans – which would have to consist of some conclusive fossil evidence of transitional ape-to-human forms. However, none has yet been found.

And the orthodox interpretation has been further undermined by a growing body of scientific evidence indicating the presence of humans on Earth long before is supposedly possible, according to the orthodox view.

Charles Darwin was an ingenious, careful and genuine seeker into the workings of Nature, but also very much a man of his time. As an Englishman in the nineteenth century, he was inevitably influenced by the ethos of the all-conquering British Empire, powered as it was by the technological successes of the British-led Industrial Revolution.

This would seem to explain his quest to come up with a *mechanism*, a machine-like account of how some species seem to victoriously survive while others fail and disappear. And his heightened awareness of rivalry, competition and conflict is hardly surprising – seen in a political context of *dominance* through *divide-and-rule* backed up with the threat of violent force.

And that within an *economic* context of fiercely competitive capitalism.

Hence his theory of species 'adapting' to their environment

through so-called *'natural selection'*, resulting in the *'survival of the fittest'*. And all this in a world of apparently *'random mutations'* appearing in each new organism.

As a superficial description of the *physical* evidence, it does seem, more or less, to fit the observable patterns through time.

But that kind of nineteenth century 'winners and losers' thinking only addresses the *physical* dimension of life on earth. It lacks a *wholistic* overview and any sense of the other, more subtle, more fundamental, aethereal dimensions of our lives.

To this we can also add the historical-religious fact that the idea of *reincarnation* had been decreed heretical by the Church over a thousand years earlier, and by Darwin's time this denial had become established belief. That gave rise to the short-sighted outlook of *one-earthly-lifetime-only*, in which to succeed or fail. In such a context, physical survival takes on a much increased importance.

Thus he found himself caught between, on the one hand, his own realization that species adapt and evolve, and on the other, the Church's freeze-frame view, that species were created by God for all time in their present forms.

This became increasingly unacceptable to him. Furthermore, his views on Nature and evolution were reportedly very darkly affected by the death of his first-born, ten year old daughter.

However, Charles Darwin does seem to have had a much less extreme and dogmatic attitude than the current neo-Darwinists, as the following quote from him shows.
"I am inclined to view the world as if it were the result of designed laws but with the details left to chance."

From our overview, we realise that if we focus only on the innumerable physical details, we fail to notice that these are all parts of a greater *wholeness*. And we fail to appreciate that the underlying patterns of flow and continuity are the workings of the *Aether*.

So, having rejected the orthodox theory of evolution, as fundamentally flawed, what to put in its place?

Here is a more wholistic, organic view.

And again, we need to remind ourselves that any <u>physical</u> examples we use to illustrate <u>aethereal</u> processes will inevitably be inadequate – because the physical is qualitatively different from the aethereal.

Now, as a limited model only, we could imagine <u>one living tree</u>, with the many species as the branches and roots, and the individual creatures as the leaves.

And this tree we see radiating outwards, as it reaches towards the encircling sun, and inwards through its roots.

Obviously, it would be a nonsense to describe the branches and leaves as 'competing' to occupy the available space – just as your fingers and thumbs don't compete with each other, but co-operate as parts of the one <u>you</u>.

➤ The main trunk and leading, *growing point* of our imaginary tree represents *humankind*.
And it carries the information of the seed from which it originated.

➤ Given the rhythmic rotation of the sun, the branches can be seen as spin-offs reaching outwards from the main direction of the growing tree.

➤ In our model the branches below the growing point represent the 'lower' species, each fixed at its own level.

➤ The higher branches represent the species closest in resemblance to humankind.

➤ And just as the seed carries the blueprint for an 'ideal' tree form to be continuously regenerated, so humankind continues evolving through successive generations towards some ideal state presently beyond our capacity to imagine.

With this broader perspective, we can see how the Darwinian view completely fails regarding the bigger and more subtle questions of <u>human</u> evolution.

For it doesn't provide a valid explanation of humanity's distinctive and more advanced modes of *consciousness* – that is, compared with creatures whose physical resemblance to humanity suggests that their consciousness should more closely resemble humanity's.

The <u>crucial error</u> has been to notice a pattern of physical similarities and progressive changes, and then rush to interpret these as a particular kind of sequence, as a direct chain of *causes* and *effects*, linking the latest model to the long-passed original version.

And here we encounter one of the fundamental scientific misconceptions of the Darwinians: ie that we, humankind, are direct bloodline descendants of apes – that the common ancestor of humankind and today's apes is an earlier ape – when, in fact, the apes are spin-offs, having branched away from the main line or stem which is *human* evolution.

Such mistakes arise from the non-wholistic attitude of seeing only the *physical* level of life as real and significant, and from ignoring even the possibility of a different scientific explanation.

And to take our line of thinking a step further, once we accept that the Aether existed before the cooling and solidifying into the material-physical universe, a vital clue presents itself.

And the clue is, that early humanity evolved first as an *aethereal proto-organism*, which then evolved into our present *physical* form.

John Wilkes's pioneering research into the vital properties of water affirms this understanding.

JW: Things move from life processes towards mineral processes, so to speak. Everything was much more *vital* earlier on. The whole Earth, as we see through our geological research, the whole Earth was more plantlike. It was *softer*.

Which opens up a path of enquiry very different from both the Darwinists' and the creationists' approach. And which doesn't have 'missing links' or non-adapting, non-evolving species.

Dr Margaret Colquhoun is a biologist and ecologist, and co-author of the book *New Eyes for Plants*. She also heads *The Life Science Trust*. And through this organisation she is presently running a pioneering ecological educational project in Scotland.

MC: I've spent my whole life studying evolution, so I could talk about it for hours and hours. I was first a Darwinian evolutionary biologist; I respect Darwin and his place. But I think there's more to it than he said. It's only part of the story.

I think life was first and the physical came afterwards, condensed out of life. And that is the opposite way round, I suppose. You can almost see that happening in embryology. In the fossil record you can see earlier forms of animals, and then primates, and then the human beings are at the end physically. But if you think of the physical stuff in the fossil record the ones that got left behind hardened and we have stayed neotenous, young. And we are like an earlier stage of development of apes. We haven't got old yet.

There are still other animals that are evolving as well. And plants. The less specialised ones are going on evolving.

It seems to be important to understand that time is not linear. And if you can experience time moving in two directions then evolution starts to be easier to understand. It's possible to think in other dimensions about it.

The future is transforming the forms of the present. So it's organised from in front rather than from behind.

For a practical engineer, a *wholistic* interpretation of Evolution is very much required. But this will be dealt with more fully elsewhere, since it is not required by this *Report*, and Evolution is such a highly complex, multi-levelled process.

So, taking a very brief *wholistic* look at Evolution raises the question: What is the fundamental _polarity_ that drives it?

And here we find a rhythmic alternating between an outward and an *inward* movement, an *expanding* phase and a *contracting* phase: an *e-volutionary* phase and an *in-volutionary* phases.

The Evolutionary phase is the *outward* movement from the hidden, inner, potential to a state of earthly *physicality* – ie from *seed to plant*, and...

The Involutionary phase is the movement *inwards* – from *plant to seed* – to contain, conserve and prepare the *potential* for its next emerging.

149

Understanding this cyclic process resolves those riddles about *'Which came first: the chicken or the egg, the oak or the acorn?'*. For such questions only arise from ignoring the *continuity* of the *whole* process – and from just focusing on the separate, *physical* bits and pieces within it.

The universal principle of *Involution* is also concerned with how consciousness – spirit or soul, to some – *involves* itself in earthly matter through incarnating into a physical body, creating a living organism.

GENETICS has become an integral part of *evolutionary* thinking. Here again it can only be referred to briefly.

The bigger context is the rhythmic pulsating of the Aether resulting from the continuous cyclic movement in the cosmos. From this comes the continuous repetition of living forms in Nature, a process we call *regeneration*. This word is closely related to the more recent words *gene* and *genetics*.

We observe how the geneticists rushed in, idealistically trumpeting many fantasy-like predictions and promises of cures for this and that and fortunes to be made, for which they did get lots of publicity and funding.

But, having reduced the whole subtle and complex business of heredity down to DNA chemistry, they then hit the reality phase. And now they're finding, just like politicians, that they simply cannot deliver on their plans and promises.

Nick Thomas and **Dr Edi Bilimoria**:

NT: The problem with genetic engineering at the moment is that nobody understands it.

EB: Yes. How does the Aether come into it?

NT: Because what they've been unravelling with genetic

engineering is the Life Aether. It's just the Life Aether that's being unravelled – well, not unravelled, sadly.

EB: Manipulated

NT: You see the Life Aether is wholistic in the best sense of the term and, to illustrate what I mean, one started off, in biology, with a conception of an organism, an organism as a whole. And then, nobody knew what they meant by wholeness. And then, by reductionism, all the problems associated with describing a complete organism were dumped onto DNA. And they said, everything's described by DNA. And everybody went, 'Ah good. We can get rid of this embarassing notion of wholeness.' And what happens? We find we have 'jumping genes' and all manner of phenomena.

The DNA, the genetic make-up, was behaving just like an organism. All the stuff they thought they'd got rid of is re-emerging right down at that level. That's Life Aether. Life is sitting right there.

And of course, the genome is supposed to be a description of that very DNA. But nobody, as we said earlier, nobody can grasp that in its wholeness. So then you're dealing with Life Aether the same way if as you look at a human being and you're only interested in his hand. And you're not the least interested in the arm, the head... And you say, 'Right, we'll apply a medicine that will have a wonderful effect on your hand.' Apply the medicine and you die, because it goes and affects the brain.

Biologist, **Dr Margaret Colquhoun** again.

MC: I think people are realising that the central dogma doesn't hold true anymore, that genes produce amino-acids produce proteins produce our characters – that's no longer true.

A brief survey of the system of thinking behind current Genetics reveals, to an engineer's eye, a very unsound, unreliable structure. For a start, there is no universally agreed definition of what a *gene* actually is – as was openly admitted in 1976, in the first presentation of the *'selfish gene' theory.*

Checking out the design behind the *selfish gene theory*, we find an inherent *ambivalence* in it – that is, signs of deeply split thinking. The theory is loaded with 'as ifs', such as references to 'the great architect' and to 'purpose' in Nature. But then these are adamantly denied having any basis in reality.

The tone is reminiscent of the over-zealous, over-rational atheist, trying just a little too hard.

It's as if someone has designed a laboratory which strangely reminds you of a cathedral or a sacred shrine.

Even Harvard professor of genetics, **Richard Lewontin**, dismissively refers to its *"unsubstantiated assertions and counterfactual claims"*.

Like the instability to be found in any system which lacks an essential, integral, balancing element, this ambivalence – this swinging between two disconnected extremes – is a typical symptom of *Aether denial.*

All of which inevitably leads us to ask: What on earth, then, is this thing geneticists call the 'gene pool'? More on this later.

Here's Nick Thomas again.

NT: I don't know if I know what a gene is.

        Over the years I've read books, I've read newspaper articles and, as long as you don't inquire too deeply, it's quite easy to imagine. You sort of imagine a string of beads of different colours, or maybe conglomerations of beads of different colours wrapped up in a spiral form. And you say, 'Oh that's a gene. That particular set of beads forms a gene.' And you may give them the correct scientific names and so on. The structural concept has been rather like that – a DNA sequence which can construct then a particular kind of protein, or something that the body needs.

But increasingly this concept of genes has been becoming fudgy. In the last few years articles have been appearing, researchers have been accepting the fact that they don't really know what a gene is. Because, where they thought there was a gene-coding for hair colour, they suddenly find it's coding for something else under different conditions. So then, what's a gene?

A gene was supposed to be that which determined a very particular trait – colour of your eyes, the length of your beard, the shape of your ears – I don't know what it would be. Whatever. It was supposed to be a very particular trait. And all of a sudden they find that the same little stretch of DNA is coding something else. That's of course exceptionally unfortunate for the mechanical view of genetics. And naturally, there's frantic re-thinking – what the economists would call re-stucturing, which is a polite term for saying you've gone bust and you're trying to re-schedule your debts and so on. Likewise in science one has to do some re-structuring and re-scheduling and that's going on at a furious pace because this is very disturbing.

So, a gene therefore is a concept. It's a pure concept that goes back to genetic theory as it was first invented in the 19th century, which of course Darwin knew about, and was part of in a way. Those concepts, 19th century concepts, were billiard ball concepts and they've lasted ever since. And we've attached this notion of a gene to a billiard ball-like concept. And we've lost the billiard balls but we've still got the concept, which people would like to apply to our universe if they don't want it to have Aether and they don't want it to have soul. It at least gives them an 'out'.

So, I don't know what a gene is.

So the *gene* is actually no more than an *idea*, a *suggestion* – concocted to satisfy the materialistic craving for a measurable particle, a unit of *hereditary instructions*. And *instructions*, of course, convey a prior *purpose*.

Here we can refer back to biologist, **Sir Paul Nurse**, and his experimental findings on *purpose* in the living cell we heard earlier.

Meanwhile, here's **Nick Thomas** – on *heredity*.

NT: Heredity is a tricky one because we've got some very fixed ideas now about what we mean by heredity. And I suppose if I was to put it at its most desperately simple I would say, our concept of heredity is a sort of photocopying process that isn't quite faithful. The one thing that does not happen when a new human being is born is that a photocopying process takes place. Photocopying processes are copying that is only on the physical plane where something is copied from one physical structure to another.

And this is why it's very important that we don't think of the birth of a human being in terms of photocopying. You know, the genes of the mother and the genes of the father are photocopied and then mixed up a bit to produce a new document.

That's how we think about it and it's very very important that we don't. Because, referring back to our thoughts about the cosmos just now, the Aetheric forces from the cosmos come in from the wide periphery and they're what form the human organism.

To an independent minded engineer, *genetic engineering* – or *genetic modification*, as it's also called – blatantly demonstrates the crude, short-term, short-sighted thinking of the materialistic mindset.

However technically clever, it's engineering of the most ignorant, irresponsible and potentially dangerous kind.

If the same approach were applied to *social engineering*, it would be about as unsubtle as trying to make an unhappy family happy, simply by extracting a happy child from a happy home and implanting him or her in the unhappy home.

From our wholistic overview, then, we can interpret these imaginary little ideas called *genes* as units of *purpose*, as the artificially divided up bits of one greater purpose, the *will-to-evolve* of one living being. And one pseudo-technical sounding name for this living being – much used by biologists – is the *'gene pool'*.

Meanwhile, the emerging science of *Epi-genetics* has clearly demonstrated how *environmental* factors have measurable effects through subsequent generations in humans and animals.

The so-called *bio-tech* industry, lacking any understanding of the healing potential of the Aether, for a while rode high on a wave of false optimism. This was generated by the over-hyped *human genome project*. And it was all in the context of the insatiable hunger for instant fixes for our many diseases. In the process it has led to some remarkable yet legalized, greed-inspired nonsense – for example, the commercial *patenting* of naturally occurring phenomena, like indigenous plants.

THE ENGINEER'S 3 TESTS

– regarding Western science and Evolution

TEST 1: SOUND PRINCIPLES?

Here is another case of flawed assumptions resulting in unsound conclusions. Orthodox evolutionary theory is based on the arbitrary generalization that life on Earth is all about *competing* and *rivalry*. And this notion continues to be programmed into humanity's consciousness worldwide through the mass media and education systems. It works on the *childhood* level of our being, whatever age we are – that stage when we're striving to find our own place and level in the greater order – by testing ourselves against others.

Meanwhile, many are now realizing that creative *co-operation* – on our shared human journey of individual and collective evolving – is the more mature, sound principle, ultimately more efficient, fulfilling and beneficial for all of us.

TEST 2: ELEGANT DESIGN?

The various strands of Western science's thinking on evolution and heredity could be better described as a tangle of misconceptions and wrong conclusions, completely lacking in *elegance*.

TEST 3: EFFICIENT OPERATION?

Within certain narrow limits, Darwin's theory has some

correspondence with what can be physically observed. BUT over-extended by Western science, it inefficiently and disastrously fails to explain the real differences between humankind and the apes, and how life on Earth actually began.

However, once we understand the *Aether's* vital role in the longer, cosmic story of our origins and history, a much more coherent picture begins to emerge.

And finally, there is, of course, the greater context of *Cosmic Evolution*, which is essential to a full understanding of earthly *natural* evolution, but is also beyond the scope of this Report.

That fuller perspective sees humankind, all the other species and the planet evolving together, through various developmental phases, into their present forms, and beyond.

NT: Well here you have, of course, a wonderful example of polarity, really, where you have the large scale interacting with the very small scale. And we have marvellous examples of that, first of all, within the human body for instance, or any organism.

If you take an individual cell, that cell is interacting and part of the total organism of the body. And the way the cell changes through its life – although that's not evolution, it's a picture to begin with – how it changes through its life, its destiny, for however long the cell lasts, is all part of a much larger whole.

What is happening in the earth is not actually divorced from what's happening in the cosmos, although we might think so. And equally, what's happening in the cosmos is not actually divorced from what's happening on the Earth. It's very difficult for us at the moment to perceive the connections. We will.

I spoke about the evolution of matter: matter will evolve on, it will become different from what it is now. That will apply to the planets, it will apply to the Sun. All of that will start changing.

And that's the same kind of thing. We are in one sense, inside the solar system, but if you go out of your body and have an aetheric consciousness instead – which is turned inside out compared with our ordinary consciousness – you find yourself looking in, and you feel the Sun as your heart, and the planets as organs of your being. And we all share them together. And you have that same kind of synergy as I was speaking about with the cells and the body.

And then we'll find that we'll have this body on earth, but we have a consciousness that's reaching over the whole solar system. And then as we change on Earth, all of us in synergy with one another, the solar system follows suit.

In this longer view of evolving human consciousness, our re-awakening to the Aether can be seen as a sign of progress towards freedom. That is, a freedom that transcends the current immaturity and distortion, a freedom in which humans consciously choose to live in ways harmonious with the rhythms of the living cosmos and Nature... of which we each are a vital part.

The *descent into matter* has left humankind with a legacy of inertia, unawareness and fear. All that this project has revealed indicates that the *ascent out of matter* is, albeit with much difficulty, well under way.

Thus we come full circle in realising the connectedness of *consciousness*, *cosmos*, the *Aether* and humanity.

Conclusions and Recommendations

We've held Western science up to the light, so to speak, to try and view it as a whole – that is, in the context of both the wider world and its greater cosmic environment. For it does not exist in isolation, and to ignore the breeding ground from which it has emerged would be negligent.

It has been found that there is something fundamental missing from Western science, and what's missing is a clear awarenesss of the Aether. So how is appreciation of the Aether being prevented in the wider political and economic context of Western science?

If we cast an engineer's eye over the wider social scene in which scientists live their lives, certain features immediately stand out – particularly to an engineer who has specialised in **control and power systems.**

Regarding _political power_: to an unprejudiced observer, it's clear that so-called 'governments' – especially elected politicians – are little more than token, symbolic figures, a distraction, kept well isolated from the effective _power and control system_. Like the ornamental moving figures on some old mechanical clocks, their function is to create the _illusion_ that it's they who make the system work.

How the hidden power systems and networks do operate in contemporary societies is not the concern of this Report.

We can see police forces and other such sub-systems as _servo-mechanisms_, maintaining the status quo just as thermostats control temperature.

Feedback loops such as market research and public opinion polls, meanwhile, help keep those in control a step ahead of the game.

Safety valves normally reduce pressure build-up. As a kind of *aetheric* technology, they allow people to let off steam – in various media forums – thereby dissipating discontent without disturbing the system.

These are just parts of a whole range of cleverly engineered *Grand Scale Illusions* for manipulating mass consciousness – made possible in the great gap resulting from the denial of the Aether. And there's one which is particularly relevant to the future of science.

Nick Thomas and **David Lorimer**:

NT: This timidity of legislators, politicians, that level of life – they're timid...

DL: I think part of the problem is that actually not very much research is being sponsored in these areas. And so people can say, 'Well there's no evidence', because there's been no proper research trials designed and funded. And so it's a bit of a Catch 22.

Catch 22 was the title of Joseph Heller's classic satire on the insane futility he'd encountered in the US military.

> What the government is doing is telling universities and scientific institutions is to get into bed with Industry. Industry have very specific agendas as to what they want to develop and what sort of research they want to do. And mostly, it's actually continuing more of the same. You look at the chemical companies or pharmaceutical companies – they're not going to want to sponsor research on organic agriculture or wholistic health, unless they can corner a market in it. And so I find it very difficult now to disentangle the influence of politics, economics and science. It's all become very entangled.

A *Catch 22*, to an engineer, is a particular kind of *mechanism* built into any system. It diverts your progress back, in a loop, to an earlier position. You are thus prevented from advancing beyond it – unless, that is, you're prepared to challenge the whole system itself and the assumptions on which it is based.

Scientists are often very quick to point out inconsistencies and falsification – in certain areas. However, regarding the hidden assumptions behind the *funding* of science, there seems to be a significant silence.

So who does control the big money, if not governments?

The global banking business has power over all national governments, because all nation states are deeply and inescapably in debt to it.

The 19th century international banker, Amschell Rothschild, is quoted as declaring:

"Let me issue and control a nation's money, and I care not who writes its laws."

So it's these banks who ultimately sponsor whatever kind of enterprises their controllers favour. And their basic working formula for continuing to divide and rule seems to be: maximise competition, rivalry and enmity in all areas of life, including the acquiring of money. For the more people are kept in endless rivalry the less they question the motives of those who take advantage of that situation.

Thus we have a world mesmerized by the illusion of this aethereal stuff called money, and effectively ruled by those who control its supply. The key word, then, is FUNDING.

And most relevant to this Report is the funding of the universities, colleges, schools and industries in which scientists work, teach and study – and where science evolves, for better or worse.

And so, from an engineering perspective, we complete the circuit, and connect back to our starting point. Bankers to governments and corporations, governments and corporations to scientists... and in return, scientists providing the technical know-how for maintaining the status quo.

We now have a working sketch-plan of the system, and a key to understanding the wider *entanglement* referred to by David Lorimer.

This planet provides more than enough natural resources to meet the basic needs of all humankind. Yet we accept being told that many necessities for life simply cannot be afforded, which makes this expression, 'cannot be afforded' one of the all time great deceptions. And it only works through the illusions created by a corrupted money system.

Meanwhile our supposedly rational analytical scientists seem either unable or unwilling to even acknowledge this gaping and technically fixable inconsistency.

In the light of all this, the question has to be asked:

Are these failings of Western science deliberate or accidental?

Is this an issue of integrity or ignorance?

Either way, it's crucial to the specific problem this Report is addressing, the negative and worsening image of Western science in the world today.

Given all that, here's **Professor Brian Goodwin's** view of where science is heading.

BG: We've strutted around in our culture as controllers and dominators of the earth and the result is the earth is going through a pretty drastic transition that's going to challenge our culture very deeply.

I think what we're going through at the moment is such a deep transformation of science that it will no longer have that name 50 years from now. It will be called something else.

Now, for me, the really exciting thing that's happening now is the recovery of qualities. As we all know, modernity, modern science, Western science, excluded qualities from the domain of reliable knowledge. And that was a perfectly sensible move in the 16th century, 17th century, and in the 18th century if you like. There was a point at which it ceased to be a very good move but nevertheless it persisted because it was so successful in the realm of technology.

Well, we cannot live without qualities. And now we're experiencing that dramatically. Quality of life is what everybody is gasping for – not everybody, but most people – and what we've done is to destroy quality so effectively that most of our eco-systems are now collapsing. So, the quality of life – by ignoring it, by seeing the world as a mechanical world of quantities, we have actually pulled the soul out of it and therefore it's dying. Our world is dying.

Now, the thing that is so exciting is that this is the moment: out of the darkness comes the light. This is where the light is actually returning. So what we have is the possibility of a 'science of qualities'.

RECOMMENDATIONS

Established institutions are, by their very nature, a form of inertia, resistant to change. This is perhaps the price of stability. But that price is always negotiable – between the established old guard and the emerging new blood.

Once the current failings of Western science have been acknowledged, humanity will be able to create new organizations which can evolve like organisms. These could be designed to include open, failsafe mechanisms to avoid any future science establishment becoming inertia-bound and corrupted.

Similarly, protocols and procedures could be developed which best serve the unity and diversity of humankind as a whole – in our greater earthly and cosmic environment.

And any significant healing of Western science has to involve re-acknowledging the existence of the Aether.

Without it, the prospect is one of disintegration into a mere historical blip in the longer story of human evolution.

The crucial question now seems to be the human equivalent of what nuclear physicists call the critical mass. That is, how soon a sufficient number of humans will be awake, aware and ready to make the necessary changes – given the present deteriorating global situation.

This Report thus serves as a red-light hazard warning of imminent danger – like a wake-up call which reminds you that while you're busy occupied with this and that, your home and neighbourhood is being infested by vermin.

Raised Aether awareness could also bring fresh insights and a long term overview to such major issues as global climate control and safe energy sourcing. So it raises some very immediate and crucial questions for each and all of us, like it or not – which we can choose to address or ignore.

Either way will have its consequences. But Western science does need to venture out beyond the defensive walls of its own castle – within which minds are programmed to see the world only in a bits-and-pieces mechanical way. It needs to learn to appreciate the rhythmical ebb and flow of continuity, of wholeness in the living cosmos.

NT: In rounding up what we've been doing, working through the Engineer's Report, one of the important points we've been trying to bring out is that denial of the Aether is having an extremely harmful effect on the whole way we think about the Earth, and indeed the way we think about each other, for that matter.

And a removal of that ignorance is really urgent.

How do we face this challenge? What are our priorities?

We need to free ourselves and begin to really re-think our whole world picture. And this can be done. It isn't just a matter of wishful thinking.

There are sound principles and bases and considerable progress has already been made in re-thinking our whole paradigm. And this re-thinking is part of taking responsibility for the Earth and taking responsibilty for each other in a way that will lead to something creative rather than something destructive in the future.

Afterthoughts on The Engineer's Report

As indicated earlier, this never was going to be a comfortable journey – more one of necessity. Nick Thomas' own words indicate that this is not a time for sheltering in the comfort zone of professional etiquette. Realizing that denial of the Aether is a symptom of a bigger pattern of denial and ignorance has made it a test of personal and scientific integrity. For ultimately, the state of science reflects the state of mind of the scientists – within, of course, their broader human context.

The *Conclusions* to the *Engineer's Report* contain a number of apparently negative or pessimistic observations. A positive way of viewing them, however, is as part of a test. We could see it as a *test* of our readiness to raise our consciousness to a higher level; or an *initiation ordeal* – as fear, temptation, distraction and deception challenge our willingness to seek out hidden truths about this living, conscious universe and our part in its evolving.

Regarding science and education, the situation outlined in the *Report's Conclusions* makes it clear that it would be of the utmost importance to any controllers of humanity to be the final arbiters of what <u>is</u> and what is <u>not</u> taught as 'acceptable' science.

In the *Engineer's Report* it was also noted that the Aether functions according to what we normally understand as *moral* and *ethical* principles. That's because the Aether is an indivisible *oneness* of which each of us is an integral part. Therefore, all our actions affect that wholeness and, to some degree, all within it.

Meanwhile, the present stark contrast between the *starving* millions and the *overeating* millions in our world exemplifies how serious the problem of *imbalance* is. It points to the need for a whole new way of thinking, a new kind of integrated science and spirituality which would make the most of our unique situation, poised as we are at the *threshold* between the *aethereal* and the *physical*.

And one essential of this way of thinking is to start from the *wholeness* rather than from the *part*. For example, a *bubble* is one whole, dynamic phenomenon, not simply reducible down to a number of component parts – as also, of course, is a living organism.

———————————

Scientist **Michael Watson** has over many years investigated the border between the aethereal and the physical:

At the Threshold of the Aethereal and the Physical

Michael Watson

The Aether is not just an abstract force like electricity is. It's got this mobility inside it which electricity doesn't have. Electricity's got one set of rules which are written down by Maxwell and it always behaves along those lines. Aether doesn't have that. It's got myriads of different rules.

The Aether is a reactive thing. Just like living organisms are, which are an embodiment of these aether forces. You look at life and you see how it works. It reacts to the environment. It's not a passive force like electricity which reacts only in one single way. It can react in a variety of different ways, and this is the aetheric force. And because it's self-organising, because it's reactive, it is the essence of what we call life.

And if you took the whole plexus of all possibilities then it would be a great big 'conscious being', if you like. But the conscious being is not a man sitting on a throne like the god-images. It doesn't work that way. This force is self-organising in conjunction with what it's got to organise against, if you see what I mean. It's an adaptive force, in other words. It's a reactive force which is completely different to any force that we know about. So, the force, in a sense, has got its own intrinsic .... *will* is the wrong word, but you see what I'm getting at. It's reactive self-organisation. So that's where evolution stems from.

The force itself has got this property within it. I mean, we're children, with playbricks compared to the actual reality of the thing. It's altogether something which is far vaster than that. But this is what the essence of it is. Don't forget, all these things are operating simultaneously everywhere, on everything, everything living.

Electricity in the days of Faraday was something completely out of the ordinary compared with the mechanical forces which they'd been dealing with. You had the horse and cart and people hitting bits of iron with a sledgehammer and that was the way technology was at that time. Then suddenly this guy comes along with a piece of wire and somebody grips it, you know. The footman turns the wheel of a huge generator and somebody grips the wire. And he'd put a whole chain of ladies round in a big circle, you know... one would have one end or the other..... And then, they touched the end of the wire and got an electric shock. Invisible fluid flowing down the wire! It's just the same thing. It's just that we've become accustomed to *this* invisible fluid flowing down the wire and we think we know all about it. We know *something* about it but evidently not *all* about it.

Physics is looking at the mechanisms of the death process, the corpse, and it's picking over the manky remains, but it's not seeing the origin. It's lost the origin. But, there is no physical means of seeing it in this precursory condition. By very nature, by definition it's non-physical. The physicalisation of it is the death of it. So all that you're doing is measuring the corpse. So, the whole of physical science, as we can see, is dealing with corpses – and the corpse of the aetheric energy. That's the beginning and the end of it. That is the root of the whole business.

Physical instrumentation will never yield knowledge of the Aetheric thing. They're mutually incompatible because of the way in which the physical instrumentation works. So you never will see the vital force with modern physical instrumentation. No matter how sophisticated, how many dials it's got on it, what computer's associated with it – even if it occupies the size of this room – they'll all work according to the same principle, which is the exchange of physical energy. And the Aetheric doesn't use that. When the Aetheric does exchange physical energy, it's dead. And once it's gone into the physical world you never know what its origin was. All that you know is that you have detected electric potential.

Now, there are physical instruments, which are not in the current line of ordinary physics, which will detect it. But it's so difficult to do and use. You've got to know what you're trying to do when you use a physical instrument for it to give you any sort of meaningful result.

If you're looking for the Chinese meridians, the acupuncture points, you get a physical instrument, a voltmeter, and you go along there and you prod an acupuncture point and you think, Ah, there's a point. You find a meridian of someone because the meter indicates. Now, you're left with a division of the ways here:

If you're a physicist you say, the meridian exists but it's none other than electro-chemical potential, a voltage produced by light processes. Why it should be in a line, I don't know. It happens. And why you should get places where it's bigger than others? Oh, it's some sort of neural thing, where the nerves meet or something like this. So you say it's a purely physical, electro-chemical process of the same nature that if I get a jam jar of salt and put two electrodes in there and put those to the meter, that would indicate as well. It's the same thing, same energy. That's it. As far as the physicist is concerned that's the end of it.

But the Chinese would say, No no, you've got the *chi* energy flowing through this point, life energy, vital energy. Science would say, No no, you've got just electro-chemical potentials. *Chi* energy doesn't exist. All energy is electro-chemistry.

But, you see what happens. In the process of detecting the *chi* energy, you've destroyed it – converted it into electricity. And the same thing is going on all the time. So, if you ask a physicist to detect one of these vital processes, he'll get his instruments out and the instruments will kill the goose that's laid the golden egg. All physical instruments, no matter how sensitive they are, extract energy from something. Kill it.

Einstein was a Master of the World of Corpses. All he's saying is that the material, gravity-bound world is a consolidation of energy and the quantity of energy is this..... So, you're dealing completely in the world of corpses. And you can forget the Aetheric.

Energy of Light is actually invisible. It's not electro-magnetic or anything else. It's the aetheric force. If you put something in its way then it becomes Light. So when it hits matter or meets opposition then it immediately physicalises – dies, that is – and becomes electricity. And the death of it gives you vision of it. And then we try and measure it.

In order to measure Light you've got to interfere with it in some way, which is tantamount to saying that you're measuring the interruption, or the darkness. And that interruption is the same thing as killing it.

You see, the Light is an aetheric force. The act of detecting it and looking at it turns it into Light, as we understand it. We never see behind it because our instruments can't see behind it and aren't Aetheric instruments. If we had aetheric eyes then we could see the Light in its reality. But we can't.

If we had a spiritual perception we would be able to see the aetheric energy coming in. We could see the death of it into electricity. Because we don't have aetheric sight, as distinct from physical sight, the concepts are missing from our vocabulary. So we're in a sort of intellectual blind alley. It's a cul-de-sac. We will never ever get out of the cul-de-sac if we go in the direction we're going. It'll just get more and more materialistic and we'll be dealing with more and more finely divided corpses. And we'll find everything we need to know about corpses but absolutely nothing about life processes.

Everything which has been living has left an imprint in the Aether, if you like, which is part of its intention field. And that's what it's building upon. And so, in a sense, it is an entity, but the entity is being created continuously by nature and intention.

This is why in all religions you have to be careful of your intention. Because your intention is building an image, and that intention will tend to be fulfilled if you're not careful. So my view of it is that you've got this huge plexus of reactive fields and man's intention seems to be particularly powerful.

Regarding that unresolved dilemma of modern physics, Is what's being detected a wave or a particle?:

Physics calls it the collapse of the wave function, because it's noted that, before the actual event of detection occurs, all possibilities which the apparatus allows are present together. Now, if you generalise that completely to the Aether, you've got a whole range of possibilities of states it could possibly be in if it was to be gravitationalised. But it collapses into one single state when it becomes converted into a physical entity. And that is the formation of the electricity or whatever it is, whatever transformation it is. But nevertheless, whatever it was before is unknowable because we only know the results of its death. (That is to say at the physical level. If you've got psychic perception then you can see both ends of it.)

The different grades of the Aether – particularly those known as the *Four Aethers* – were first distinguished in a Western scientific way by **Rudolf Steiner.** Born in 1861, he was trained in the sciences and was also deeply involved in the creative arts and education, a combination felt to be very important by the next contributor.

Ecological research biologist, **Dr Margaret Colquhoun** works very intimately with the natural world and the Aether.

She is presently running an active ecological and educational project in Scotland.

An Ecologist's View of Aetheric Science

Margaret Colquhoun

I studied Biology at Edinburgh University and I have a first degree in Zoology with Evolutionary Biology and Population Genetics. And then

I worked for a while as a Research Associate studying seaweed flies and population genetics throughout Britain and round the coast of Scotland. And then I did a PhD in the evolutionary biology of small mammals on islands off the coast of Britain.

I love science and I love orthodox science; it's necessary to have that in order to go beyond it, to stand on. In conventional academia, I found it quite restricting because I always felt as if I was coming up against a kind of brick wall, when you wanted to go into realms of life or spiritual things. I found I needed to go into another dimension in order to satisfy my knowledge and my experience of Nature. I discovered then that there was a way of doing this through Goethean Science and I went to Europe to train in this for four years. And since then I've been teaching and researching with Goethean Science in Britain.

I feel that this wholistic approach embraces orthodox biology and it just adds a new dimension. All science is subjective – that's probably very provocative. But scientists don't usually recognise that it's the subject that's doing the science. In Goethean Science the subject is important and you acknowledge your subjectivity. And then it becomes objective.

When I trained in university I was taught that with the conventional, modern, scientific method you can never prove anything's true. All you can do is set up a hypothesis and disprove it, knock it down. And when I discovered this wholistic way of doing science, my experience is that in that process you become aware of a self-evident truth in whatever you're looking at, which is the antithesis of knocking down a hypothesis to prove it's *not* true. And that's very hard to grasp unless you have an experience of it. And when I studied in Germany and Switzerland this was one of the hardest things for people to get hold of.

How you think, how you use your mind as an adult, is using the same forces that grew you when you were growing. And if you train the use of those forces, which are the powers to think, then the working of Aether within yourself and within the world becomes a tangible reality. And one thing that's very interesting is that I've met quite a few people who, when they start doing this kind of training, on the development of their relationship or use of Aethers within themselves – they grow. And that's a very extraordinary phenomenon, as a middle aged adult to find that your hand size, your head size, your feet size, is all getting bigger. And you actually get bigger in bone and stature. So something happens to your own Aetheric body in the process of transforming your cognitive capacity, which is the same Aether on another level. Quite a few people have experienced this and I was warned this might happen when I embarked on my training. My feet size changed by two sizes, from four-and-a-bit to six, and I got a little bit taller and a bit broader.

What most of us do normally – if you see someone who's tired, you offer them a chair. Or if you see them drooping a little bit you might go and get them a cup of tea. Or you recognise that a plant needs water or that an animal needs some kind of attention. There we're recognising a depletion in life and we immediately react. The awareness is there in everybody but, training it and tuning it to see the physical, you notice spiritual things that you might not have noticed before.

I experience that, when you recognise something of life, or the first level of spiritual awareness, you see it manifested in the physical world as well. So learning to read the signs in the physical is a training, a training in consciousness and perception which anybody can do. It's like switching on a switch. And it's training you to be aware of the obvious. And when you start seeing like this you just say, 'Oh, I always.... Why didn't I see that before?...I've always seen like this but I wasn't aware that I was doing it.' And I think it's a part of making conscious the obvious.

Women and children and artistic men – this will sound very

prejudiced – seem to do this very much more easily than people who've had a scientific training. Because they start to *think* very carefully about it and then you can't just *feel* it, which is what you need to do if you're trying to tune in to a growth process.

If you're trying to understand how something came about or get closer to something in Nature, then you might start with the first impression of it, or the *mood* of a place or a plant, which has something of the quality of its atmosphere. But it's guided by fire or warmth of interest or love. And then slowly as you look at it you come down through its context, its life context – where it's growing or how it's grown – until you can really see it physically. And then, if you had *immediate* spiritual consciousness, you'd be able to see its essence straight away, but most of us can't, so we have to go on quite a long journey where we work out physically what is there. And the more you look physically, especially if it's with plants or something in Nature, you start to be aware of a life process within the physical. And you almost can't avoid moving from this physical dimension into something which is growing.

You have to change your consciousness from the exact sense perception to something which is like imagination. And that quality of tuning into the growth or the life of something is using the *Tone Aether* or the *Chemical Aether* in your thinking or your imagination.

And as you go through that and it's working within you, it starts to take on certain shape, and you realise that the *pattern* or the *music* that this particular being of plant or landscape is playing in you, has a quality which is unique to it. And once you start to see this movement in a different way, or in its own special way, you get a kind of 'Ah ha!' experience. *That is* a dandelion or *that is* a daffodil. You suddenly wake up to its being or its essence; something lights up in you and you recognise *that* for what it is. And I think that has something to do with this quality of the *Light Aether* – in you.

If you go into science being as human as you can, using all

your faculties as a human being, then it becomes artistic. And if you do art, also trying to become conscious of what you're doing in the creative process, you become scientific.

If you look at marigolds, or calendula... if you go near to marigolds in the garden, you have a very strong experience of a kind of strong warmth coming from them. It's a bit pungent and there's something very powerful in it, in this colour and in the smell. And this kind of envelopes you and makes you feel very whole.

When you start to look at a plant, you draw it, you look at it growing and study how it develops, and then look at its chemical constituents, look at what it tastes like in a tea or how it works on you if you put it in water – all of these are using your senses and then your imagination. And you come to a very deep *knowing* of this plant. But you don't have to take it necessarily, destroy it and analyse its molecules. It's more gentle. You are analysing, but not in a brutal way. You could say that the gentle empiricism is plant-led rather than scientist-led.

I think if you do this path with a plant and you come to connect to its essence then that's... for me the most important thing is, then you become morally responsible. And if you were making a medicine, or if you were wanting to work in the landscape in a particular way, or with animals, then you have to be... you feel a way of doing it which is *incumbent* upon you. You can't do what you want any more. It's as if the plant tells you what to do with it. And that is a kind of 'becoming at one' with something which sets you on fire. And it gives you this sense of moral responsibility which is extremely humbling.

If you've done lots of work with, say, calendula, and then you've made a cream or a medicine, a tincture, and you need to show statistically how many cuts get healed when you put your thumb in the water. Then you can use statistics to show it on that level. But it's speaking another language. There's a place for it but it's not in studying the plant. When you study a plant and you want the plant to tell you what it's used for, then you use science to really come to the essence of the plant. And then the art that comes out of that is that you need to find out a way of capturing the essence of the plant, in the bottle or cream or whatever. So there's a whole process of *condensation* of an idea into something practical that you can then use as medicine.

And the other example that you saw today in Pishwanton is that we use this way of looking at landscape to come to a consciousness of what used to be called the 'genius loci' or 'spirit of place' and then try and create a space, a place, out of that experience which will clothe the activities that want to happen there. And that then becomes a building. And that creative process is how we've *condensed the picture of an atmosphere* in Nature into a building – to clothe activities that we want to do there.

Maybe you could say that learning to experience the Aether is a way of listening rather than speaking in Nature. And letting Nature say what *it* wants to do, rather than you saying what *you* want to do. It's the beginning of starting to work in partnership instead of …*counter.* I don't think we'll be here if we don't start doing this.

I've spent my whole life studying evolution so I could talk about it for hours and hours. I was first a Darwinian evolutionary biologist. I respect Darwin and his place. But I think there's more to it than he said; it's only part of the story. I think life was first and the physical came afterwards, condensed out of life. And that is the opposite way round, I suppose. You can almost see that happening in embryology: in the fossil record you can see earlier forms of animals, and then primates, and then the human beings are at the end physically. But, if you think of the physical stuff in the fossil record, the ones that got left behind hardened, and we have stayed neotinous, young, and we are like an earlier stage of development of apes. We haven't got old yet. There are still other animals that are evolving as well. And plants. The less specialised ones are going on evolving.

It seems to be important to understand that time is not linear, and if you can experience time as moving in two directions then evolution starts to be easier to understand. It's possible to think in other dimensions about it.

The future is transforming the forms of the present. But you don't know what it's going to be yet. And that's a bit like... there's a direction in evolution which had to do with humans happening... or apparently, or so far. And that's determined what happened before. So it's organised from in front rather than from behind.

The gene's become a fuzzy concept. I think people are realising that the central dogma doesn't hold true anymore – that genes produce amino-acids produce proteins produce our characters. That's no longer true. There's quite a bit of work where people show that something akin to what was called Lamarckianism is happening. And the gene is only fixed in its context within an organism. So if you shift it from one organism to another, which happens in genetic modification, or genetic engineering, then you don't know what's going to happen – it changes, it produces something different or does something different in another organism. And that's playing havoc with the concept of genetic manipulation because things start happening that people could never have predicted and don't understand. And that brings up lots of questions.

On one level, probably nothing harmful does happen. But then, what happens on the level of the inside of the organism? What happens on the level of the whole environmental context? And what does that mean for the evolution of plants as a whole? So they're really big questions. I think it has to be looked at in a much bigger context.

If you just listen to normal people – they know. So many people won't touch genetically modified food now, and there's an inbuilt feeling or *knowing* that it's not right, on a certain level.

We don't have the tools as conventional scientists to explore this. You have to explore it on a much deeper level because we're interfering in Nature in a way that's completely unprecedented. It's never happened before. And the scientists say, It's not our responsibility. The Government set up working groups but they say, 'We are not able to be responsible because we don't have enough knowledge.' And there is nobody who is taking responsibility other than the people who are wanting to make money out of it. And then it becomes unethical.

Until there is a science developed that is ethical and responsible, I don't think we can judge it. Often people in scientific laboratories abdicate responsibility; they do their job very well but they don't actually take responsibility for what happens afterwards. It's like, you can split an atom but you don't take responsibility for its use in a bomb. And this is the same kind of thing. Where does the responsibilty sit? And we haven't worked that out yet as a society, and we are in a realm that we... it's running away with us and the people who have the power are the people who are making money out of it.

Personally, I wouldn't ever knowingly eat anything that had been genetically modified.

The aethereal aspect of food and nutrition has been referred to by the twentieth century spiritual master, **Omraam Mikhael Aivanov**. He spoke of how the glands on and under the tongue extract the aetheric energy of the food and how, with the very first taste, long before the food has been physically digested, we can begin to feel energised and nourished. The aethereal qualities of flavour and aroma have also been considered by various others.

Pre-physical

Acknowledging that the Aether does exist also involves realising that it's *pre-physical*, that it came into existence before the physical universe. As such, it's the all-inclusive *context* from which the physical world emerged and within which it functions. It's the intermediate level between the lower *physical-material* and the higher *cosmic-spiritual* levels.

This is why we don't experience the Aether directly through our *physical* senses. What we do is *infer* its role in producing certain recognizable patterns of *effects* in the physical realm – whether in our own bodies or in the world around us. This is somewhat similar to the way we can 'read' a person's body language or, from physical signs, understand some of the deeper processes of Nature.

We use a special kind of awareness to sense this universal presence in which our feelings and thinking happen. And it's on this subtle aethereal level that we are able to appreciate the coherence or wholeness that does exist behind the fragmented and apparently random material world. Perhaps it's what some call our *sixth sense*.

Increased awareness of the Aether by no means amounts to a complete 'theory of everything', but it is an essential part of humankind's maturing and evolving. And it's the key to a deeper understanding of *healing* which essentially means *making whole* or *holy*, and includes healing ourselves, others and our world, on all levels, physical, psychological and cosmic or spiritual.

Re-acknowledging the existence and power of the Aether could liberate Western medicine from the death-grip of both materialistic science and the various greed-driven industries that presently dominate it, for they've reduced it down to a mechanistic technology of short-term symptom targeting.

Yiannis Pittis is a full-time healer and teacher of healing and esoteric knowledge. He has dedicated his life to this work.

Esoteric Healing

Yiannis Pittis

Since I was able to travel then I began my travels and journeys, and I met many wonderful beings – healers and teachers all over the world – who imparted to me the benefit of their experience, their teaching.

And I synthesised and integrated that and now I am able to share from the benefit of that experience and help other people also. So this is in brief what the journey included.

However, to describe the meeting with these magnificent and remarkable beings – it would take many lifetimes and many books and it is not possible to convey it. All I can say is, in meeting them, it is like meeting your divine spiritual Self, for they are fully able to manifest that divine immanence in their radiance, in their aura, in the love that they emanate from their Heart Centre, in the selflessness that you see around them... And this is evident, not only because I perceive it in their aura, but also in the way that they deal with those that come to assist or to ask for help or to be healed.

My first encounter was really during the hours of the night, when I would travel to a place in the Himalayas and meet a certain being which I subsequently came to know as my Great Teacher. And there, there were other beings like me who would receive teaching and then we would come back. And whereas, in the daytime, other children wanted to play football and run around and do other things, I was looking forward to go home and put my body to sleep and go up there and learn more about these magnificent things.

So very early I realised that there is an external knowledge, and an inner knowledge that is not so easily accessible even in the academic schools of our world. And so I very quickly chose to search for that inner knowledge continuously in my life rather than dedicate myself to studying in university. So I have no degrees. I have no pieces of paper that say I am this or I am that. I am just a peasant boy who has spent a lot of time researching the inner aspects of life – our constitution, religions, and what really can allow us to be free from suffering. So that is what I have taken on board as my calling and my destiny: to the best of my ability assist other human beings to liberate themselves from suffering and to find the way of harmonising their actions, their thoughts and their emotions to the laws that govern manifested existence.

Aetheric vision – anybody really can begin to trigger it. It's not so difficult. Everyone, when we do some lectures on healing or aura and so on, I give a simple practice, and then we have pretty much a ninety-nine per cent success of everybody being able to see the 'aetheric body' – that glow that is around the physical form. And most people are able to see it, once they are relaxed enough and, instead of looking with a direct focussed attention, they use more the lateral, widened sort of perception, like relaxing the eyes and, instead of focussing on anything physical, you just allow the impressions to flow in as if you were gazing at a distance. And slowly this wider range begins to awaken and then you begin to pick up this aetheric glow.

There are two levels to the aetheric glow around the body. There is that which is interpenetrating the physical form and that which is outside the physical form. That which interpenetrates the physical form is a bit like – every physical atom has its aetheric counterpart. Yes? And that which emanates beyond the physical form, then it is purely on the aetheric level, and it has two layers to it: one which extends approximately, I would say, about half an inch out of the skin, and then that which people often call the 'health aura', which extends a little bit further, maybe two to three inches, depending on how highly charged the person is, or energised, or exhausted. If you are exhausted it goes closer to the skin level. If you are more energised it expands further outwardly.

Let us not get lost in the names, but the concept and the idea and the reality is what is important. There are four basic elements on the physical plane, and there are four counterparts to the aetheric plane. They allow us to have different functions. Without them being present in our bodies, certain experiences of sensual and nerve level functions would not be able to happen. So our nervous system works in perfect accord with these aetheric minute channels which are like nerve endings – they are called *nadis* in the Sanskrit, or 'sacred aetheric channels' in the Western language. And energy flows through them from major stations that are called 'centres' or *chakras*, through finer threads and then into the nervous system.

And the co-operation between the nervous system and these aetheric channels is a perfect system, which is known by yogis and Taoists. They call them 'meridian lines' and 'meridian points'. And a lot of our health problems and suffering depends on the quality of these fine aetheric channels. If they are blocked then energy is not flowing. If the energy does not flow then certain of the organs do not receive their due. And if they don't get what they need then they begin to become exhausted, more vunerable to infections, more vulnerable to diseases. If they get too much, exactly the same problem is created – an imbalance. So, an imbalance of one kind or another, either by exhaustion or oversupply, can create that phenomenon that we call a disease.

The aetheric body can be wounded. So, if you have a physical wound then that will show in the aetheric wound. If you have been wounded aetherically, then eventually that will actually manifest – not instantaneously, but pretty quickly – on the actual physical as well.

So, what wounds the aetheric body? Tremendous shock, a mental breakdown, drugs.... I don't mean medical drugs, although they have their side effects, but mostly other drugs that, unfortunately, the youth of today are taking on board without knowledge of the damage they are doing to this fine aetheric body. They predispose then, the aetheric body – they open little holes, little leakages. You call them wounds – they can be called so. Intense fear, intense panic, intense sorrow, intense hatred – all of these powerful emotions affect the aetheric, because the aetheric is connected with the emotional or astral, as it is called. It's not separate.

To begin with we must start with appropriate breathing. In the in-breath and the out-breath there is an exact opposite polarity. So when you are breathing in the lungs are expanding. When you are breathing out you are apparently emptying internally but feeling the space externally. And so there is constantly this 'tick-tock' between the inner space and the outer space. So, in our inner space there are gravitational forces that penetrate our inner space, as they exist also in the outer space. What name will we give to the opposite force to gravity? Levity. That's why one of the powers which are known as *siddhis*, or psychic powers, is levitation.

But levitation is not only on the physical plane. There is also levitation as a spiritual consciousness into a higher dimension of awareness and higher planes of perception. So, ultimately it is an expansion and an outpouring or an outflowing from the centre. So, we can say that life moves in rhythmic motion, from the centre to the periphery and back to the centre again. The aspirational forces that we emotionally have, also can generate this levity. Aspiration is a very human quality, and to the degree that we have it, to that degree we can bring about that elevation.

The vitality energies or life forces that are flowing through these subtle aetheric channels can be maintained in better health by better breathing. So I try to teach people how to breathe more effectively. Because so many ailments would be minimised if we were able to breathe more effectively and we were able to bring into our 'aetheric double', or our 'aetheric vehicle', greater levels of the pranic life forces. They will benefit in health, for a start. They will benefit in terms of being able to have preventative medicine, because the disease is seen first of all on the aetheric double and then it manifests on the physical. So imagine being able to go to the doctors and they have developed a fine machine that can look at your aetheric body and take, like a form of X-rays or a form of MRI plates, but on a more subtle level that we call Aetheric. They would be able then to *prevent* diseases. And so we would benefit in terms of advancement in the medical research, in terms of advancement in our own health and wellbeing.

Within the next ten to twenty years I think we will have that advancement already coming. Now, Kirlian photography and all of these things are the precursors or the forerunners to these more advanced systems. The technology already exists. It's a matter of making the right demand. And when you make the right demand then the supply will be provided.

Actually this is the principle on all levels: if you make the right demand, internally, for higher spiritual energies, then they will be supplied. It's all a matter of the law of supply and demand – on the physical plane as well as on other planes. It's a matter of acknowledging it, knowing it, and then with conviction, demanding it or calling forth, or invoking it, another word would be. And then it will come to pass. Ultimately, the idea exists, the technology exists. It's just a matter of blending these two and having the demand and it will happen.

If people put articles, or books or discs or whatever, out that talk about the 'aetheric double' and the 'aetheric body', and that our health and wellbeing on the physical plane depends so much on the health and wellbeing of this fine aetheric vehicle, and people then start asking questions – 'Well, what kind of practices must I take on board to ensure that my aetheric body is healthy and better?' And then teachers begin to give that information out. The whole momentum can be built up for the greater research, the greater scientific equipment, and so on and so forth.

I think that it's very close. It's a matter of people building a bridge between the more concrete levels and the finer levels, and then being able to assist people to cross that bridge.

There are two kinds of clairvoyance: the low clairvoyance, which is like a basic thing that people call a hunch or a gut-feeling. And sometimes, by birth certain people will be able to have that lower clairvoyance. Now, science finds it difficult to believe that within the human framework there are latent faculties that can be awakened, can be triggered, consciously and through appropriate and safe kind of exercises and practices, where then one can have a control over these faculties and use them as it is appropriate.

184

The higher clairvoyance is operated through this particular centre of energy which is known as the Brow, or in Sanskrit, the *ajna*, centre. Of course, it is connected with the so-called 'Third Eye.' This is *not* the Third Eye; the Third eye is something completely different, but you cannot have the higher clairvoyance unless the Third Eye *is* awakened to a certain degree. This Third Eye, according to my understanding of it, is the blending of vibrations generated by three major centres of energy in our head. One is the Crown, the top of the head, one is the Brow, and one is the Alta Major, or the centre that is at the back of the head.

When these energies become activated and radiant, not only on the Aetheric plane but also on the Astral and Mental planes, their fields blend and they create a glow in the centre of the head. This glowing light is actually what is being transmitted, or directed like a torch, to illuminate areas of enquiry in the Mental or Astral plane, or Aetheric plane. So there is Aetheric vision, there is Astral vision, there is Mental vision and there is Spiritual vision. And each one of them uses a higher part of our consciousness or a lower part of our consciousness and a corresponding physical organ which may be dormant at a certain stage and becomes active at another stage.

The higher clairvoyance is something that is unfolded only when a human being genuinely purifies their physical form, their emotions, their mental form, and their attitudes and moral awareness. That is the foundation. Without that foundation, the higher clairvoyance, the higher telepathy, does not become awakened.

Supernormal consciousness

Here's a clip of engineers, **Nick Thomas** and **Dr Edi Bilimoria**, discussing supernormal powers and secrecy:

NT: You see, there are certain people who have a very natural entry into the aetheric realm by direct experience. And then come up the possibilities of magic and misuse. Now, what happens is that those people can wrap up their discoveries in such a way that other people can't penetrate them. You know, it's a kind of imprisonment.

However, if you can penetrate through to those same truths by ordinary human capacities, then you undo the wrapping. And I feel my task is that. And so I don't have any very special experience other than in my realm of thought, where I seem to have a natural ability to think about this clearly. At least, I think it's clearly.

EB: What you're doing is, in a sense, removing the veils and lines.

NT: Yes. And I think you can do that with your ordinary consciousness.

EB: So it's more accessible.

NT: That's right. Because the time is going when the most important knowledge must be secret. The time is coming when the most important knowledge has to be understood by everybody, because that will then bring a protection of its own. I mean, contrast the notion of a few people who discover nuclear power and don't tell anybody. And so nobody knows about nuclear power and one day suddenly there's a huge atomic explosion and ghastly things happen. Contrast that with the situation we have today where everybody who has any kind of education knows about nuclear power and has opinions about it. And then the protection comes in because now you can't do things in a covert way.

In the continuous recycling of living nature physical death, summarised very briefly, can be understood as a process of progressive releasing or shedding. Our individual aetheric body is absorbed back into the greater ocean of the Aether. And what was the physical body is left as inanimate, disintegrating matter, to be re-united with the earth. The process then continues with our more subtle levels of being. This timeless knowledge survives in many cultures outside the bounds of the narrow materialistic mindset.

Dr Geoffrey Douch is a very experienced medical GP, homeopath and anthroposophical doctor, practicing both in London and Sussex, England.

Here we have a combination of Doctor Douch speaking and some quotations from his booklet on Anthroposophical medicine.

Aetheric Medicine

Geoffrey Douch

You're brainwashed, basically, when you've trained to be a doctor. You end up thinking you can cure everything. And it's just not true.

'.... anthroposophical medicine comprises knowledge of the human being, including the spiritual aspect.'

'This medical system was one of the earliest to adopt a holistic approach and remains to this day one of the most comprehensive.'

I'm a normally qualified medical practitioner, worked many years in general Practice. I've had a special interest in homeopathy and anthroposophical medicine from quite early on in my career, and studied at the Homeopathic Hospital and did the normal post-graduate qualification in homeopathy.

I came into medicine really... full of ideals and, you know...how wonderful it all was and how clever we were – to become fairly rapidly disillusioned when I went into General Practice.... and began to look for something else. Well, I didn't have to look very far because I'd already met these things. But, basically, discussing it with a friend, another doctor who was already a homeopath and an anthroposophical doctor, urged me to take up the study of it more full time. And at that point I went to the Homeopathic Hospital and qualified in homeopathy, studying anthroposophical medicine at the same time.

The Aether, in terms of Anthroposophical thinking, is something which permeates basically the whole universe, and which supports life where it is possible – that may well be in other places apart from our Earth – and becomes more specialised, as manifest in life, animals.... all forms of life, basically.

Among other things, obviously, that one thinks about as a doctor... one can, to some extent, have an idea of people's general vitality – of which the Aetheric forces are a major part at the level of nutrition and one's physical make-up. And you can form an impression that people have, 'a weak Aetheric body' or 'a strong Aetheric body', because obviously, some are better equipped than others. And clearly also, experiences in life affect one's Aether body as well.

Visualising the Aether forces in a clairvoyant way is not something *I* can do, but one has to make deductions from what one discovers in people's history and make-up and so on. And I feel quite at home with that. In a way, it's only the *effects* of the Aetheric forces that you can study – the effects of its action in life, in plants and animals and man.

Homeopathic remedies are absorbed into the fluid part of one's organism, which is the realm of the Aetheric forces.

> 'Homeopathic, that is, potentised medicine, has the virtue of acting more directly on the human being than conventional or herbal medicines which have to be potentised by the body before they can exert an effect....'

There's matter... it's matter with Aetheric forces which makes a living entity. That's how I see it.

'Anthroposophical medicine distinguishes a fourfold structure of the human being.

Firstly there is the physical body which is composed of the material substances of the natural world.

Secondly, the human being has a body of forces which he has in common with the plant world. This provides the life forces which are known as etheric forces and they operate through the medium of water – hence life is dependent on water......

Thirdly, the human being possesses a body of forces which enliven the physical and and etheric in such a way that these become capable of sensation and feeling..... This body is known as the Astral, and the Astral forces operate via..... constituents in the body such as air or dissolved gases.

The fourth part of the human being – and this is the one which distinguishes the human being from all the other kingdoms of nature – is the Ego. This gives the human being his individuality. The Ego holds the balance between the other forces, particularly the astral and the etheric. The medium for the ego is warmth.'

The idea of polarity is certainly very basic to Anthroposophical medicine. And normally one is thinking of that more in terms of the nervous system, say, and the metabolic system, which means the polarity between Astral and Aetheric, really. Combined with the other concept of an Astral body... I mean, that whole series of concepts completely *re-vitalised*, I suppose you could say, my interest in medicine. I mean, it completely transforms your attitude to the patient. And things which from a conventional point of view are regarded as trivial, are often really interesting to the homeopath or the anthroposophical doctor, because any disturbance from normal is a pointer to some sort of imbalance between the elements of the Aetheric body, or between the Aetheric body and Astral.

Whereas the conventional view is really virtually a hundred per cent materialistic, despite protestations about wholism and so on, the whole thing with the anthroposophical, homeopathic view is...really, entirely comes to life, and it becomes a whole absorbing issue.

I mean, if it weren't for that I would have retired from medicine long ago.

Homeopathy

Nick Thomas again:

NT: I can say a little bit about homeopathy, because I've had a lot to do with that, and what I've discovered really is that, what we were talking about in more abstract terms as waves, tone and so on – this is music. The cosmos is filled with music. And this so-called Tone Aether, Chemical Aether, it's actually the 'music of the spheres', as it's sometimes called – a wonderful poetic phrase. And when you go into this other consciousness that's what you experience. You're surrounded by the music of the spheres.

And in homeopathy, what happens is that you draw the music into the substance that you want to make. Because the music heals. And so you draw that music into the substance, and when you do that you have a healing..... well, you have a *powerful* substance. It depends who draws it in and for what purpose as to whether it's healing or harmful. That's always of course – what we talked about before – that two-edged aspect of the Aether as a whole.

John Wilkes has long been researching the life-enhancing properties of water and has his own research institute in Sussex, England. His invention, the *Flowform*, is featured in many places around the world.

Water and the Aether

John Wilkes

I'm not using, sort of, Aether language very much, but I think we're talking about the same thing.

When I think about the effects that one can bring to water – sensitising it through rhythms in such a way that its quality is changing – this seems to me to be enabling water to reconnect itself with this Aetheric *living* world, in the context of the fact that, whatever we're doing with water, mechanically and chemically and so on, is disengaging water from this realm. What I was discovering, I think, was that....and this is underscored by other people who have much more experience than I.... that one was sensitising the water. And I've really understood this world of rhythm as being a kind of gateway. Water is there as a medium which is mediating these Aetheric forces, if you like, to the organism.... is *enabling* the organism to be embedded within its environment, not only physically but spiritually. And this is the theme with which I'm trying to work.

At school I was very interested in science and chemistry. And I prepared to... Well, no, I have to say first... a teacher appeared who was an artist, who in a sense drew me out of that realm and showed me what I could do artistically. And so, I was going to be studying architecture and I'd prepared for that. But in the meantime I found that there was an Art School, a very good College of Art, at Wolverhampton, next to where I lived. And so I went there. And from there I went to the Royal College in London.

I always was very impressed with Jacob Epstein. And the reason for that is, whenever he worked with something, it was the idea which he was grappling with. It wasn't Epstein who was promoting himself. Wonderful man. And we knew him at the College when we were there and I learned a lot from that relationship. And of course I was meeting people like Henry Moore and Brancusi. These main people, you know, they were really quite extraordinary people. The whole world opened up – all *this* world we're talking about. And through that I came back, through the artistic world, to also a scientific world. So that's been the influence upon my life – that I'm working really with art and science. And when I was teaching here I was always saying, 'Art needs some Science, and Science certainly needs some Art.' This is where the future lies.

I'm particularly interested in the whole question of movement. Now movement carries the essential things. Every form in our world is created through processes of movement. And this is brought about, and the physical world is based upon, the fact that we have polarity.

At a certain point in evolution, you might say.... they're only pictures really, but .... contraction appears. If you think of the spiritual world, you don't see anything, you don't hear anything, if you like. There's only emptiness. But as soon as contraction as a capacity, as a quality, enters, the whole of this process becomes possible.

So that contracting processes leads us to the possibility of a physical existence. But you can't only have contraction. You have to have expansive forces as well. So that every aspect of the physical world has something to do with contraction and expansion. So things are harder or softer. Now this is really movement. You can't have movement without polarity because there's always a balancing act going on between the two tendences of contraction and expansion.

And so movement is born and within that realm of movement you have rhythm. And rhythm then leads to the phenomena we have in the world which we talk about as metamorphic. Metamorphosis is really the physical, gelled activity of rhythm.

And so this was for me one of the essential questions: Could I provide for water a vessel, or even I would say, an organ.... this was my first question which led to the work I'm doing with Flowforms... could I provide a vessel which would enable water to manifest its capacity to order and metamorphosis?

And I put that question in the context of water moving through Nature, where there are always so many influences that that order doesn't really appear very clearly – say, if we look at the river or the mountain stream, there's a cacophany of rhythm in there. Through that the meandering process is born. And that also is this adjustment continuously of the left and the right handed – the erosion and the deposition within the meander, and so on.

So that's for me a very essential thing which really led in the direction that I'm moving. And I'm trying to work, of course, with these Nature processes but take them in the direction of an emphasis through the fact that a human being is involved. I'll just say what I mean there: in the river, in the mountain stream, which is the most wonderful experience of water we have, there's this cacophony of rhythms, but now if we can pull out of that cacophony of rhythms the specific rhythm, we then are entering the living world. Because in every living organism you have a very specific rhythmical process.

I discovered what led me then to the Flowform work, which was mainly discovering that if vessels were proportioned in a certain way rhythms would be generated. So that really started off my life's quest.

We have done experiments, for instance – we allowed water to fall over steps. So that's dominantly under the influence of gravity. Then we let water fall, again through the effect of gravity, through vessels which then generate this oscillation through the fact that they have certain proportions. And so you get a situation where the water is being momentarily rhythmically lifted out of gravity into a levity realm. It's this swinging process. I think we can say, it's not only gravity. It's a levity process as well.

And the effect upon the water, interestingly enough, is that where gravity dominates (and this is with a certain species of plant we used in a project in Holland) the water dominantly under the influence of gravity is water which seems, in that particular circumstance, to support *vegetative* processes. So those plants were full of leaves. Just a bundle of leaves with very little blossom. But the water which was rhythmically treated supported plant growth of a much lighter quality and fewer leaves and far more blossom.

So you get this *vegetative* support or *generative* support in the plant. But this was done over a number of years and is one direction which we're tending to follow up. This changes the quality of the way the water supports the plant in the terms in which I was talking before – that water is the medium bringing these things to the organism. When the plant is dying on the window sill it's dry, and when you wet it, it's not just a matter of making it wet, it's a matter of linking it again with its environment. That's the essential thing.

We have to work very strongly towards a new consciousness for water. It's the blood of the earth. I think that's one of the essential things. I think we're going to have major, major... well we have already, but... we're going to have much more difficult problems into the future if we don't change our consciousness to water. Because water has this extraordinarily strong relationship to movement and through that also to this Aetheric world. Nothing can function actually without it and so it's very much encapsulated in this whole thought.

And I think what we're interested in is trying to awaken in people a completely different attitude to water – that it's a most precious substance and it has these capacities which I've already talked about, of this mediating, this *intangible mediation*, you could say, between the environment and the living organism. We have to open up to that otherwise we'll be lost. Nothing can happen without developing consciousness of these things. Terribly important.

Obviously there are always individuals who are opening up to these things and they usually have quite a difficult time in the scientific community – people like Benveniste, who were just outcasts. But then other people come along and prove that he's correct.

The whole of our physical evolutionary process is due to the fact that there was a vital, spiritual content there to begin with. Things move from life processes towards mineral processes, so to speak. Everything was much more *vital* earlier on. The whole Earth, as we see through our geological research, the whole Earth was more plantlike. It was *softer*.

And we're reaching a point more and more... in a sense in the nineteenth century – this whole materialistic and physical-dominated attitude develops.

And then since then, the interesting thing is that suddenly you have the development of Modern Art – the great masters of Modern Art. Where people are beginning to say, What is Movement? What is Form? What is Light? What is Colour? Abstract Art was *the* art, the naturalistic art, of the nineteenth century.

Real investigation of *real* things started in the realm of Modern Art. That's not abstract at all! What is Form? – that's not abstract.

They were creating sculptures – the Cubists and, whatever you like, the Impressionists, all these different streams within the realm of Modern art... this urge to investigate all these different qualities and possibilities... That's dealing with reality. There's nothing abstract about that. It's only called Abstract because people are so used to looking at things 'out there' in the natural world, and from the nineteenth century, trying to make a description of that. That's not art any longer. It's completely abstracted from everything spiritual and everything else.

And when you do a portrait – I was very involved in portraiture – you don't copy the person. You're really trying to discover what are the essential aspects and elements and qualities within that person. And through form you're trying to express those things, or through colour, or whatever.

A Bigger Picture

Having now touched upon various topics, perhaps the best way to complete this project would be to take a broader look around and leave open some of the many questions that have inevitably arisen.

First, what is the essential core or thrust of this project?

The intention has been to help re-awaken awareness of a reality long neglected in this materialistic age, the Aether, and so reconnect with our cosmic origins and roots. The risk is accepted that this may at first be unwelcome to some.

If we accept the possibility of the Aether being pre-physical, we gain the potential for a much longer and broader view of our evolvement and history.

Power struggles

Given that the Aether is pre-physical and *the matrix for new forms*, early humanity would have consisted of conscious, *aethereal* beings in a more aethereal planetary environment than now exists. And according to various myths and legends, there would have been conflicts, some of which have continued into our present time.

This view gives us clues to the ancient power struggle for dominance of humanity still being waged from behind the cover of religious, national, corporate and other flags of convenience with their various symbols and logos. And it does give some perspective on the current so-called 'global war against terrorism'.

We've seen how 'nuclear power' can be understood as the misconceived releasing of *aetheric* energy. The present struggle for global supremacy regarding nuclear weapons is, therefore, essentially about the Aether.

We can also begin to interpret various ancient texts as symbolic indicators of greater processes and realities, rather than just believing or rejecting them.

Humanity's 'descent into matter' – that is, the immersion of our consciousness deep into the material world over a vast timescale – has enabled us to learn much about this realm. However, in the process, we've somewhat lost our feel for the bigger cosmic-spiritual picture. We tend to imagine that things everywhere and at all times must resemble what we've become used to within our limited earthly horizons and timescales.

Polarity and Balance

Aether awareness enables us to experience an exquisite sense of balance and poise at the threshold between the *aethereal* realm and the *physical* realm. That is, between *levity* and *gravity*.

In terms of *human* character qualities: being overly affected by *gravity* results in a materialistic, hard, rigid attitude. Being overly affected by *levity* results in a loose, vague diffuse kind of outlook.

The characters of, say, *Satan*, representing the extreme darkness and density of *gravity*, and *Lucifer*, representing the extreme lightness and rarity of *levity*, separately personalize such imbalances. And together they portray *evil* as a polarity of imbalance – that is, of lost balance and poise.

Taking a practical approach to this, a lack of Aether awareness diminishes our overall sense of wholeness and integrity, so that we see a polarity as a split. We then find ourselves left adrift, pulled and pushed between the two polar extremes. From which it would follow that the way to overcome evil is to actively maintain our balance, harnessing the combined power of the two tendencies or forces.

The major issue of *globalization* can also usefully be seen in terms of *polarity*. The basic choice is between centralized control in the hands of an exclusive, self-interested few... OR inclusive, de-centralized power shared throughout the whole system for the benefit of all.

The cleverest con

Suppose your life and thinking are already being subtly manipulated on the aethereal level, and higher, in ways not beneficial to you. And suppose this includes your being successfully persuaded that there is no Aether or aethereal level ... or anything beyond. Then you'd have little or no chance of countering any such manipulation, either as an individual or collectively.

If this were the case, wouldn't it be just about the cleverest confidence trick we could fall for?

In an interview in 1991 Nick Thomas spoke of 'the battle for the aetheric realm'. This is the ongoing conflict to determine what kind of principles will prevail at the subtle aethereal level of our world – and thus affect all aspects of life on Earth. And it underlines the special significance of the mass media, which do powerfully influence how we see, think about and treat our world.

So, given the dangers of humanity being kept 'in the dark' about the Aether and other vital knowledge, one subject which does urgently require some special attention is the mass media. (Education is another such subject, as David Lorimer and Nick Thomas have indicated, but that's beyond the scope of this project.)

Media Studies & Propaganda

Is there a connection between the exploitation of the Aether, as the medium of thinking and ideas, and the whole murky subject of propaganda?

The *mass media* – the broadcasting corporations, the press and the many agencies operating in the *Internet* jungle – are the connection. Each basically acts as a *medium* through which is filtered a particular perception of the world, then distributed on a *mass* scale.

The mass media have become such a familiar feature of our contemporary world that, through regular repetition of their particular messages, their *influence* on mass thinking seems to pass largely unquestioned.

The kind of impression of the world they *propagate* for mass consumption is essentially their *propaganda*. And to believe that there is no subtle medium, no Aether, through which this is transmitted, could be seen as a very dangerous form of denial, of self delusion.

All contemporary issues are being intensively worked on through the mass media (and therefore, through the Aether). For the big priority now is to be 'winning over hearts and minds'.

The mass media corporations are owned or sponsored, and controlled, by groups of people who are unknown and unaccountable to the public whose thinking they are continuously influencing. Between them, they've created a great *aethereal arena* we could call the *world stage*. And it's they who decide from moment to moment which events and people are to be featured on it... but even more importantly, *how they are to be portrayed*.

So, from behind the frontages presented to the public, that is, from behind their wide range of informative and entertaining output, the real message subtly filters through. And that message is: *You are powerless to change the wider status quo, so don't even think about trying.*

The main business of this global industry then – at least superficially – is communicating through the Aether.

Communicating what? is a much bigger question. Meanwhile, many talented individuals, for all kinds of motives, compete for prestigious, glamorized and well paid careers within this industry. The basic deal is that you have to comply with certain taboos and restrictions on subject matter. You have to be complicit, an accomplice.

Related to this is the mass media presentation of the so-called 'news' and wider political debate. **Professor Noam Chomsky** has eloquently described how the mass media perform their role:

> *'The smart way to keep people passive and obedient is to strictly limit the spectrum of acceptable opinion but allow very lively debate within that spectrum – even encourage the more critical and dissident views. That gives people the sense that there is free thinking going on, while all the time the presuppositions of the system are being reinforced by the limits being put on the range of the debate. '*

This could be the motto of just about every news corporation. For the so-called 'news' is essentially an arbitrary selection of reports put together to shape public opinion in a certain way. And through the Aether it's pumped out round the clock, and effectively sustains the impression of a confusing, fragmented, disconnected world.

And it would seem to be part of a worldwide policy Chomsky calls 'manufacturing consent'. It also includes the shallow pretence of 'unbiased neutrality' claimed by certain broadcasting organizations.

Seen in this context, all political reporting, discussion and debate in the mass media is to some degree rigged. Consequently, the present versions of democracy are looking increasingly like interactive gameshows of *Pretend Politics* – with pretend governments and pretend 'people power'. And the winning teams are those most successful at repackaging and selling to the voters the old, 'more-of-the-same ' agenda – as required by the sponsors of the show.

However, the more instantaneous, nonlocal, and therefore *aethereal*, all this communicating becomes, the more volatile and radically changeable the whole world becomes too.

In the bigger context, all this about the mass media can be seen as dealing with obstructions and distractions from our main quest, which is to know more about the Aether. It's a bit like parents wanting their child to enjoy a healthy and happy childhood but having to deal with the many ways this aspiration can be thwarted.

It's also one way we become aware of the ever-emerging life force of the new encountering resistance in the inertia of the established order. The result is a continuous adapting and evolving. And one way we delay our own evolving is by staying preoccupied with the ground level details of a situation... at the expense of gaining any kind of overview or bigger picture. Here are a couple of examples:

Sex and money

Two subjects which do seem to be of some passing interest to human minds, namely sex and money.

Regarding sex: The gap in our consciousness left by the missing Aether has resulted in the disastrous split between the earthy and the sublime, between the profane and the sacred, concerning sex.

The rhythmic interplay of the polar opposite forces of the cosmos – as they move to re-unify – produces spiralling movement, whether in air, water, outer space or in ourselves. As outlined in the *Polarity* chapter of the *Engineer's Report*, these forces are known, for example, as *gravity* and *levity, yang* and *yin* or the *masculine* and *feminine principles*.

The power of the rhythmic energy that pulsates through the physical body at the climax of fusion, known as orgasm, indicates a superphysical, natural force. Yet sex is often described in terms of the non-living, inanimate, mineral realm, such as magnetism or electricity, when what we actually experience is very much the opposite of how an electric current affects us.

Now what is it that we associate most closely with the materialistic way of life? Probably *money*.

Aethereal money

Who really controls the supply of money?
And what is money, really, anyway?

Just consider how many people today, worldwide, are involved or employed in the business of money dealings – trading, lending, borrowing and gambling – convinced that living on Earth would be inconceivable without it.

The *Engineer's Report* reminded us that money is *essentially aethereal*, an idea, a concept. It flows, circulates, enables and transforms. And it takes form as a wide range of tokens, which we gain or lose for all kinds of reasons.

So, money can remain an abstract, aethereal idea – as numbers stored in computer memories – or it can be converted into action, cash or other material things. This *materializing of an aethereal* idea, and vice versa, can be seen as demonstrating the interchangeability of energy and matter, as established by Albert Einstein. Oscar Wilde's ironic angle on this was to point out how some some people seem to know the price of everything but the value of nothing.

But money evolved into *a something* in its own right, a tradeable *commodity*, and has been used to manipulate people 'en masse' for centuries. So long as we remain convinced that life could not

202

continue without money, as we know it, and that there will always be a shortage of it, we'll remain spellbound, in its thrall.

This is part of the masterful trick being performed by the worldwide network of central banks, which have somehow obtained the legal right to create and issue money-as-debt... out of thin air, out of nothing, out of the Aether. And in so doing, they appear to be official State institutions – with names like the Bank of England and the US Federal Reserve – when they are, in fact, privately owned, profit-driven organizations.

Nick Thomas,

NT: When Rothschild said 'Let me issue and control a nation's money and I care not who writes its laws,' one gets an idea that money is being manipulated. One gets an even, perhaps, more interesting idea of that from Lord Stamp when he said the modern banking system manufactures money out of nothing: 'The process is perhaps the most astounding piece of sleight of hand that was ever invented. If you want to be slaves to the bankers and pay the cost of your own slavery then let the banks create money.'

Now that's an astounding statement. And Lord Stamp was a Director of the Bank of England at one time.

Where does money come from? And what gives money its value today?

And I think we all know very well that it is no longer gold or silver that gives it its value. It's something much more aethereal. It's actually human confidence. My £20 note has its value because I'm absolutely confident that if I walk into the grocery store down the road I can buy groceries with that £20. Because the people in the grocery store think that if they take the £20 off me they can go and spend it on something else

somwhere else.

And so we have the whole network or cycle of confidence. And confidence is not physical; confidence is aethereal. It's something that lives in human beings, in their thoughts, their feelings, their evaluations.

It would seem we're talking about a huge *confidence trick*, somehow connected with *'protection'* by the State in what could be seen as a syndicated protection racket of global proportions. The *State* basically means those institutions representing the present *status quo* of power, wealth and privilege.

In this view, taxes would be the obligatory protection payments, and the funding of so-called 'welfare' would be a calculated concession granted to offset discontent.

Since virtually all new money is created as *debt* (and debt is aethereal, just as confidence is, as Nick Thomas has pointed out) the outcome is a world collectively sinking ever more deeply in debt to the global banking business, its stranglehold very much part of the 'culture of death' referred to earlier. For it's this artificial, <u>imaginary</u> scarcity that keeps the rest of humankind competing and fighting, turned against one another... ie divided and ruled.

Yet the alarm bells have so far remained strangely muted – and not least from the economics, financial and business experts. But there is no universal principle – no scientific or spiritual 'law' – that says the world has to be this way. It's all about the power of having access to vital knowledge and the powerlessness of not having it.

And given the general approach of this project, the question remains open as to how those in control of the global banking business are themselves controlled and motivated. For there is no arbitrary upper limit on what can or can't be questioned, despite the continuous attempting – through the mass media and education systems – to <u>limit the range</u> of questioning.

Need or greed

And here, we are unavoidably led to another fundamental *moral* choice.

Do I opt for a world based on real, human need... OR one based on artificially stimulated greed arising from ignorance and fear?

To deliberately avoid such a choice would be a cop out.

Professor Brian Goodwin highlights a large scale, practical example of how to disengage from the global money racket through the transition stage of alternative currencies.

BG: Now, money is not the root of anything, but it is a significant factor at the moment in the way we live our lives. And I think that what we will see is a pretty dramatic transformation in economics, with a kind of diversification of currencies, so that different communities will adopt currencies for different purposes: they can be time banks, they can be alternative currencies that are primarily designed to provide opportunities for education so that no money changes hands but services change hands. We'll need an accounting system, so we'll *talk* about money but it will be symbolic.

The Japanese are innovating in the area of currencies and health care and integrating health care and community and having essentially what they call 'happy hours', credits – people give a service to the Health Service and in return they will get other benefits. And so there are exchanges that occur within the system that depend upon currencies that are not based on the yen, not based on the internationally trading currency, they're local. They are state-run and get away from the scarcity of the international money supply. And the Chinese are now doing the same thing.

Knowledge is power

If ideas and thoughts are real, the Aether is real.

Through raised Aether awareness, we <u>can</u> transcend such artificial divisions as *sacred* <u>or</u> *secular, consciousness* <u>or</u> *matter, subjective* <u>or</u> *objective*. We then find that these pairs of opposed ideas are actually complementary – within the wholeness that is the Aether.

If knowledge and information bring *empowerment*, ignorance and disinformation bring *disempowerment* – which inevitably leads to discontent, fear, insecurity, greed and so on. And the power of propagating information and ideas through the Aether is now being appreciated and exploited as never before – for all manner of motives.

And with the *Internet* now a kind of materialization of the Aether, virtually all existing information is becoming accessible to all humanity – in varying degrees of good or evil intent, and of accurate or distorted presentation.

Given this whole scenario, appreciating the dynamics and qualities of the Aether enhances our powers of discrimination. For once we've seen through lies and deceptions – whether other peoples' or our own – there's no going back to a state of unknowing innocence.

So humanity now has the potential, at least, to decide whether or not to continue being kept in ignorance, and consequently, whether or not to continue being exploited as a disposable resource, unaware of much bigger power games being played out.

And beyond the Aether, infinitely more awaits. Available, it seems, is power and subtlety of a scale presently unimaginable. So with our Aether-based overview, we find we now have a choice. And this would seem to be part of the *testing* of humanity referred to in the Afterthoughts on the Engineer's Report where it was shown how apparently negative factors can be seen in a positive light.

We may even grow to feel grateful to the exceptionally dedicated exploiters of human frailty – for acting as our testers – and come to the decision: 'Enough is enough of that game, thanks. It's time to move on to the next level.'

We can allow ourselves to be imprisoned in an immature 'us-versus-them', divided and ruled world... OR we can transcend this and evolve into a more mature level of consciousness, enriched by our awareness of the Aether.

Appendix A

Aether and Inspiration

We live in Aether and Aether lives in us. So what could be more natural than that we should respond to images which remind us of this relationship?

Author **Richard Adams**, gives us (in his introduction to a collection of tales called *The Iron Wolf*) his vivid picture of the web of story within which we all live: 'I see in fancy.... a shining globe, poised in space and rotating on its polar axis. Round it, enveloping it entirely.... is a second, incorporeal, gossamer-like sphere – the unbroken web – rotating freely and independently of the rotation of the earth. It is something like a soapbubble, for though it is in rotation, real things are reflected on its surface, which imparts to them glowing, lambent colours.

Within this outer web we live. It soaks up, transmutes and is charged with human experience, exuded from the world within like steam or an aroma from cooking food. The story-teller is he who reaches up, grasps that part of the web which happens to be above his head at the moment and draws it down – it is, of course, elastic and unbreakable.... The web moves continually above us, so that in time every point on its interior surface passes directly above every point on the surface of the world. This is why the same stories are found all over the world, among different people who can have had little or no communication with each other...'

One of the best known, best loved storytellers of recent decades was **Joseph Campbell**, a renowned teacher and authority on world mythology. He said of certain potent images that they provide 'qualities that point towards certain realisations.' Such images arise in different cultures: 'This speaks for certain powers in the psyche that are common to all mankind.'

Marsilio Ficino, mentioned in the Introduction to this project, was a writer influential in his own time (the Fifteenth century) who inspires present day readers. As the psychologist, **Thomas Moore**, who has studied Ficino's work says, 'It is possible to realise how thin the ether of historical time is, and what a splendid conductor of imagination, allowing Ficinos to speak directly to our modern, everyday concerns.'

One characteristic of Ficino's work, which gives it such power, is his consideration of the various aspects of Aether and their effects on human spirit and psyche.

Valery Rees is an authority on Ficino and has translated his letters. She has written that, for him, Aether was 'the cosmic equivalent of spirit in the individual' having a 'mainly fiery and starry nature, which vivifies and causes all motion.' And 'what is true for the spirit in the individual can be considered on the larger scale of the world and quintessence or aether.'

In Ficino's own words: 'Just as the power of our soul is brought to bear on our members through the spirit, so the force of the World-soul is spread.... through all things through the quintessence, which is active everywhere, as the spirit inside the World's body...'

He described its character, 'In its power it is less of an earth nature and more like water, or air, or most of all the fire of the stars.' Our individual spirits can be so attuned to the world spirit that, 'The whole world is alive, and we may drink in its spirit.'

From the stream of writers who have expressed their awareness of the Aether we have selected only a very few examples. And this selection does not happen to include any examples from Science Fiction or Fantasy though, of course, these are rich in experiences beyond the familiar physical-material world.

Naturally, the creative stream of artists includes not just writers but musicians, sculptors, dancers and painters who have striven to catch the light, to capture vibrancy and vitality and the dynamics of colour and form.

The aethereal aspects of music – rhythm and flow , the expansion and contraction of sound, the expressive qualities of tone, the ways in which forms and structures arise – gradually or explosively – are easy to appreciate. Just as with the other artforms, everyone can think of many examples of composers, compositions and performers.

Vivaldi, as one instance, was able to imbue Western classical form with a luminous and immediately affecting vitality; and Vaughan Williams is one among many able to conjure atmospheric qualities. Differently, but just as aethereally, forms arising from subtly changing patterns are found in Oriental and African music and in Western minimalist composition (as Patrick Dixon has mentioned).

And, on the power and significance of song, perhaps it's appropriate to quote Ficino again. He considered how '...it pours out from both the imagination and the heart at the same time..' and said, 'You will allow that there is a wondrous power in an aroused and singing spirit.'

Of painters, here and now, we name only two:

Turner conjured waves, mist, billowing smoke and spurting steam, blazing suns, stormclouds, furnaces, so that we can almost feel the elements and the Aether. And **Van Gogh's** spiralling, twisting strokes of vital colour evoke the invisible dynamism of the Aether.

After these examples from Western culture, a brief glimpse into Chinese **Tao**ist thinking, since the art arising from it contains so many images of the aetheric forces.

'The Tao... is a seamless web of unbroken movement and change, filled with undulations, waves, patterns of ripples and temporary 'standing waves' like a river. Every observer is himself an integral function of this web. It never stops, never turns back on itself, and none of its patterns.... are real in the sense of being permanent, even for the briefest moment of time we can imagine.... In a strong wind clouds change their shape fast. In the slowest winds of the Tao the mountains and rocks of the earth change their shapes very slowly – but continously and certainly. Men simply find it hard to observe the fact.

....Each human being himself is woven out of a complex system of totally mobile interactions with his environment.....

It is only useful convention which justifies even our seeing a man, a tree, a rock, as a 'thing' instead of a set of surfaces, each of which represents changes and transformations as they go on.....

Two of the most important aspects of the intuition of the Tao are, first; that nothing which happens, no event or process, ever repeats itself exactly. On the ordinary human scale this is obvious, if one stops to think. Only on the microscopic scale, where invisible sub-atomic particles are isolated as 'snapshot' concepts, may they seem to repeat. But, in fact, the overall context of even such minute apparent repetitions has changed while they were happening; their nature is anyway 'vibration'.

Second; this immense web consisting of rolling change does not itself change. It is the 'uncarved block' devoid of any definable shape, the 'mother', matrix of time, including both 'being' and 'not being', the present, future and vanished past – the Great Whole of continuous duration, infinite space and infinite change.'

To complete this small but, hopefully, evocative collection here are some words by **Thomas Traherne** a Seventeenth century poet. These few lines from the poem, *Wonder* convey his sense of an animating spirit within – we might say, of aether within matter:

'I felt a vigour in my Sense
That was all Spirit: I within did flow
With seas of Life like Wine.'

In another poem, *My Spirit*, he again expresses his experience of
this animating force:

'.... being Simple, like the Deity,
In its own Centre was a Sphere,
Not limited but everywhere.
It acts not from a Centre to
Its Object as remote;
But present is where it doth go
To view the Being it doth note....

A strange extended Orb of Joy
Proceeding from within,
Which did on ev'ry side display
Its force;
And being nigh of Kin
To God, did ev'ry way
Dilate its Self ev'n instantaneously,
Yet an indivisible Centre stay,
In it surrounding all Eternity.
'Twas not a Sphere;
Yet did appear
One infinite: 'Twas somewhat everywhere.'

Appendix B

A Few Books Concerning Aspects of the Aether

Author	Title	ISBN
Adams, G	Physical and Ethereal Spaces	0 85440 328 0
Bailey, A	Telepathy and the Etheric Vehicle	0 85330 116 6
Colquhoun, M & Ewald, A	New Eyes For Plants	1 869890 85 X
Douch, G	Anthroposophical Medicine (pamphlet published 2002 by Roy Wilkinson, Forest Row, E Sussex)	
Lehrs, E	Man or Matter	0 85440 430 9
Marti, E	The Four Ethers	0 935690 02 6
Schwenk, T	Sensitive Chaos	0 85440 170 9
Thomas, N	Science Between Space and Counterspace	0 902636 02 3
Wachsmuth. G	The Etheric Formative Forces in Cosmos, Earth and Man (1932)	
Wilkes, J	Flowforms – The Rhythmic Power of Water	0 86315 392 5

Appendix C

4 Aethers

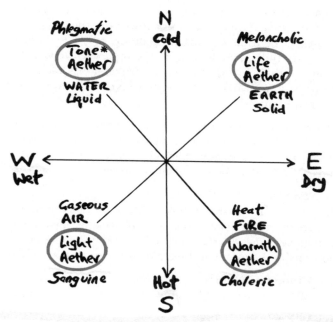

* Tone Aether: aka Chemical/Sound/Number/Colour Aether

NB It's only a diagram.

An understanding of the Four Aethers was first outlined by
Rudolf Steiner and subsequently developed by the following authors,
Dr Ernst Marti: The Four Ethers (Schaumberg Pub'ns Inc. 1984)
Guenther Wachsmuth: The Etheric Formative Forces (1932)
NC Thomas: The Four Ethers (unpublished paper)

Appendix D

A Few Pioneers in Aetheric technology

These are a few of the committed, courageous scientist-seekers who have explored unorthodox paths in the quest to better understand the nature of life – as distinct from the non-living – on Earth and in the wider cosmos. In so doing, they have risked incurring hostility and rejection: for example their reputations being attacked, their work being ridiculed, and in some cases severe persecution when they seemed to pose a threat to some established positions.

So we have to beware of any reported judgements of them and their work – either favourable or unfavourable – and focus on what they were actually investigating... with whatever limited resources they had at their disposal at the time.

Isaac Newton 1642-1727
Studied the two fundamental polaric forces of the cosmos, the inward-seeking *(gravity)* and the outward-seeking *(levity)*. Also studied *alchemy* in which is sought the ideal balancing of proportions in the essential threefold nature of all manifestations.

Franz Mesmer 1734-1815
Worked with emanations of energy from organisms and minerals.

James W Keely 1837- 1898
Controversial designer of a motor claimed to require no external material power supply. But it only worked when he was present to operate it. In that pre-Quantum era, orthodox science did not yet have the notion that the very presence of this or that person subtly affects set-ups of very delicately balanced forces.

Yakov Narkievicz-Iodko 1847-?
Developed an early pre-electron technique of 'electrography' of organic energy emanations.

Nikola Tesla 1856-1943
Genius-pioneer-inventor in early electricity developments, originated alternating current technology and much more.

Rudolf Steiner 1861-1925
Science-trained, multi-disciplined educator, first distinguished different levels or grades of the Aether, particularly the Four Aethers. Expounded the idea of the living Earth long before 1960's Gaia theory.

Viktor Schauberger 1885-1958
Pioneer in water research and the polarity of *implosion* and *explosion*, acknowledged water as the blood of the living Earth.

Louis Rota 1886-1952
Discovered a 'universal current' of non-electromagnetic Earth energy which he thought controls the manifestation of matter

Wilhelm Reich 1897-1957
Medical doctor and natural scientist, discovered Orgone energy which he likened to the then discredited Aether.

Dr Ernst Marti 1903-1985
Swiss medical doctor, made a lifelong study of the Aether, developed understanding of the 4 Aethers in *Das Aetherische*.

George Adams 1894-1963
Scientist, mathematician, wrote *Physical and Ethereal Spaces* (1933,1965)

George de la Warr 1905–1969
Engineer, in the 1940s-50s developed a camera which photographs emanations from living bodies for diagnostic applications with results comparable to late 20th century MRI scanning.

Appendix E

E = mc² – A longer view

The validity of Einstein's famous equation $E = mc^2$ was called into doubt in the *Engineer's Report*, once it was put that there is no so-called 'speed or velocity of light' – that is, the c factor in the equation. The equation itself is an upgraded version of an earlier 19th century one, $E = mv^2$ which dealt only with mechanical energy.

$E = mc^2$ is essentially an attempt to quantify the relationship between mass or matter and energy. It does not address what these are or how they originate. It assumes that we know what we mean by these terms. Yet, according to various eminent physicists such as Richard Feynman, we don't.

The ancient timeless wisdom speaks of a primal source of what we might call *potential energy* giving rise to the mass or matter, which has evolved into our present material world – as the result of immensely powerful cosmic forces exerted over immeasurably long timescales.

In such a context, $E = mc^2$ can be seen as a new formulation of this, presented in a mathematical-scientific style. But it leaves us with c^2 as a meaningless symbol – representing the non-existent *velocity of light* multiplied by itself, and serving only to balance the equation.

Following engineer Dr Edi Bilimoria's distinction between *precision* and *accuracy*, the c^2 is inaccurate in that what it represents is not a universal constant however precise the measurements involved.

Thus $E = mc^2$ begins to look like an *inspired compromise*: a *compromise* because it's based on a false assumption, *inspired* because it does, however, point towards a deep ancient truth about energy and matter. And Einstein was known to be a spiritual/ religious man.

Looking back with the benefit of hindsight, it seems quite possible that Einstein deliberately opted for such a compromise. For he would have been well aware of the general denial, at that time, of the Aether, the existence of which <u>he</u> continued openly to affirm. But perhaps, as an enthusiastic young man, he didn't appreciate the dangers of feeding such powerful knowledge into a world lacking the wisdom and maturity to handle it responsibly.

However, and for whatever reasons, once accepted and adopted by the Western science establishment, $E = mc^2$ soon became a central dogma of 20th century physics. But to an open-minded engineer, it looks like another example of *The Emperor's New Clothes*.

If, alternatively, the constant in the equation were the ever-present, all-pervading *Aether*, it would then be logically and scientifically consistent.

Nick Thomas has re-presented the c part of the equation, in mathematical terms, as a *scaling constant*, demonstrating the dynamic relationship between the *aethereal* and the *physical* realms or spaces.

Nick Thomas on E = mc²

We were talking at one point about Einstein's famous equation, $\boldsymbol{E = mc^2}$, which says that *energy* can be equated with *mass* times the square of the *velocity of light*, or perhaps better put, if you have a certain *mass*, m, it's equivalent to an amount of *energy* equal to m times the *square of the velocity of light*.

Now, if I take *mass* as relating to, very firmly, the physical side, the normal spatial side of existence, and *energy* as being related much more to the aethereal side of existence, that's not too preposterous because if you ask any honest physicist he'll tell you he doesn't know what energy is. I mean, there are lots of circular arguments or definitions like, energy is the capability of doing work. And what is work? Well, work requires energy.

So, nobody really knows what energy is. We know how to convert one kind of energy into another and we've got all sorts of magic numbers that tell us how that's done. But what actually is energy?

Well now, the whole way we've been looking at the aethereal, a new kind of physics based upon taking the Aether seriously, has led me to propose that this number c, which is a huge number - 186,000 miles per second, in good old fashioned units.

This is thought to be a velocity. And I have come up with an alternative explanation for c. I don't think it's a velocity at all. I think in fact, it is a scaling constant. It tells me how processes going on in space are linked to processes going on in 'counterspace' or 'negative space'.

And to give you an idea what I mean: if you have a seesaw, and you push one end down by one foot, the other end goes up by one foot. But supposing instead, it isn't a seesaw but a lever. And perhaps you go down one foot at one end and you only go up one inch at the other. This is of course the principle of the crowbar or the lever. Now, the scaling is completely different because you've got a a lot of movement and not so much force at one end and a lot of force and not so much movement at the other.

So, somehow, if you imagine that's an analogy for processes going on in two different spaces linked together, (so the crowbar represents, if you like, this linkage between the two spaces – and you musn't imagine they're linked by crowbars really, of course, but imagine it represents that...) then if we set in train some sort of movement and process in space, if there is such a linkage, we will set in train a movement and a process in counterspace.

But the issue is, How are they related? Does a big movement in our space cause an equivalently big movement in counterspace? Or is it like the crowbar?

And c? What I'm proposing is that this magic number c, is not actually a velocity at all. It's a scaling constant. It tells us how to relate processes in the one space to processes in the other. And it isn't a simple number because the two spaces are qualitatively different. And if you're going to try and relate the two spaces then you have to somehow bridge the fact that they are *different* spaces. They are not the same kind of space. And that's why you have such a scaling constant.

Appendix F

Aether/Ether Words & Spellings

Aether: refers back to the ancient Latin, Greek and its earlier, broader, timeless meaning.

Ether: a 20th century spelling more associated with Western science and a specific chemical substance.

(A)ethereal: having the essential status or quality of the (A)ether. Eg Like a *central* position

(A)etheric: refers to the dynamic, energetic aspect of the (A)ether. Eg Like a *centric* force.

The (A)etheric: is used by some as an all purpose name for the realm of the (A)ether.